Maths

Age 6-7

Contents

Activities

Quick Tests

Paul Broadbent and Peter Patilla

Numbers to *20*

The numbers between **12** and **20** are **teen** numbers.

They all end in **...teen**.

11 and **12** are made from a ten and ones,
but do not end in **teen**.

13 → thirteen

10 + 3 = 13

1 Write the words or numbers for each of these.

a   15   →

b   18   →

c   11   →

d   17   →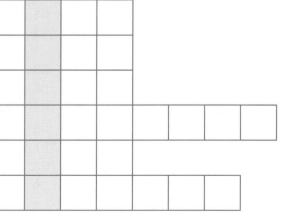

e   fourteen   →

f   nineteen   →

g   twelve   →

h   sixteen   →

2 Write the word for each number.

a 13 →

b 12 →

c 18 →

d 17 →

e 14 →

f 19 →

The hidden number in the shaded area is ☐ .

Counting

Use this grid to help you learn the **order** of numbers to 50.

1	2	3	4	5	6	7	8	9	10
11	12	13	14	15	16	17	18	19	20
21	22	23	24	25	26	27	28	29	30
31	32	33	34	35	36	37	38	39	40
41	42	43	44	45	46	47	48	49	50

1 Fill in the missing numbers.

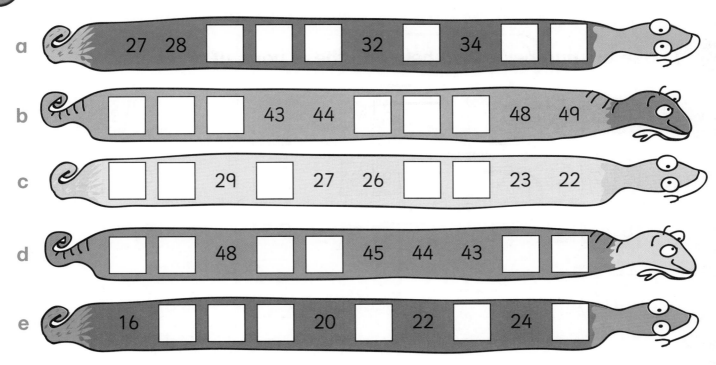

a 27 28 ☐ ☐ ☐ 32 ☐ 34 ☐ ☐

b ☐ ☐ ☐ 43 44 ☐ ☐ ☐ 48 49

c ☐ ☐ 29 ☐ 27 26 ☐ ☐ 23 22

d ☐ ☐ 48 ☐ ☐ 45 44 43 ☐ ☐

e 16 ☐ ☐ ☐ 20 ☐ 22 ☐ 24 ☐

2 These are all part of the 1–50 grid. Use the grid at the top of the page to help fill in the missing numbers.

a

	☐		
14	☐	☐	
	26	28	☐
	35	☐	☐
	☐		

b

22	☐	☐	
32	33	☐	36
☐	☐	44	

c

			10
	18	☐	
	☐	38	40
	☐		

Adding

A **number line** can help with addition.

What is 4 added to 7?

Start with the biggest number and count on.

7 + 4 = 11

1 Use the number line to help add these pairs of numbers.

a 6 3 → ☐   e 6 6 → ☐   i 3 8 → ☐

b 5 7 → ☐   f 9 5 → ☐   j 6 7 → ☐

c 8 4 → ☐   g 4 9 → ☐   k 8 5 → ☐

d 7 2 → ☐   h 7 8 → ☐   l 7 7 → ☐

2 Draw a line from each addition problem to its total. Colour the star with no matching addition.

a 40 + 2

c 35 + 5

e 23 + 23

g 38 + 3

i 39 + 4

f 41 + 6

b 20 + 30

d 40 + 8

j 41 + 8

h 22 + 22

40 41 42 43 44 45 46 47 48 49 50

2-D shapes

A 2-D shape is a **flat shape**.

Learn the names and number of sides of these shapes.

triangle	quadrilateral	pentagon	hexagon	heptagon	octagon
3 sides	4 sides	5 sides	6 sides	7 sides	8 sides

Rectangles and squares are special quadrilaterals.

1 Draw lines to join the shapes to the correct name.

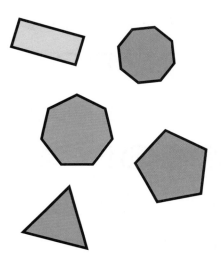

triangle

rectangle

pentagon

hexagon

heptagon

octagon

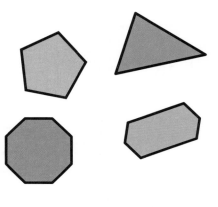

2 Colour this stained glass window using the colour code below.

 triangles

 quadrilaterals

 pentagons

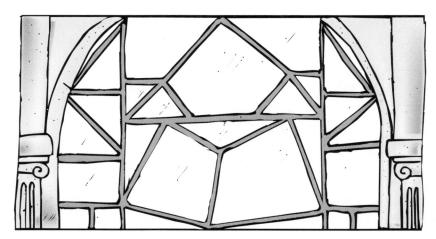

Taking away

You can count back along a number line to help you **subtract**, or **take away**.

What is 14 – 5? Start at 14 and count back 5.

$$14 - 5 = 9$$

1 Show the jumps for each subtraction. Then write the answer in the box.

a 11 – 4 = ☐ ①②③④⑤⑥⑦⑧⑨⑩⑪⑫⑬⑭⑮

b 13 – 5 = ☐ ①②③④⑤⑥⑦⑧⑨⑩⑪⑫⑬⑭⑮

c 12 – 7 = ☐ ①②③④⑤⑥⑦⑧⑨⑩⑪⑫⑬⑭⑮

d 16 – 7 = ☐ ⑥⑦⑧⑨⑩⑪⑫⑬⑭⑮⑯⑰⑱⑲⑳

e 18 – 6 = ☐ ⑥⑦⑧⑨⑩⑪⑫⑬⑭⑮⑯⑰⑱⑲⑳

f 17 – 6 = ☐ ⑥⑦⑧⑨⑩⑪⑫⑬⑭⑮⑯⑰⑱⑲⑳

2 Make the answer to each subtraction match the number on the star.

a

30 – ☐

☐ – 12

42 – ☐

☐ – 13

☐ – 18

b

21 – ☐

☐ – 17

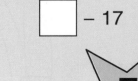

39 – ☐

☐ – 16

47 – ☐

Numbers to *100*

This grid shows the numbers to 100.

Use the **tens** to help you read and write the numbers.

20 twenty   60 sixty

30 thirty   70 seventy

40 forty   80 eighty

50 fifty   90 ninety

1	2	3	4	5	6	7	8	9	10
11	12	13	14	15	16	17	18	19	20
21	22	23	24	25	26	27	28	29	30
31	32	33	34	35	36	37	38	39	40
41	42	43	44	45	46	47	48	49	50
51	52	53	54	55	56	57	58	59	60
61	62	63	64	65	66	67	68	69	70
71	72	73	74	75	76	77	78	79	80
81	82	83	84	85	86	87	88	89	90
91	92	93	94	95	96	97	98	99	100

1   **Circle the correct number for each of these.**

a thirty-eight   83   37   78   38   30

b fifty-four   44   50   46   45   54

c seventy-nine   97   17   79   76   96

d sixty-two   52   26   60   62   80

e eighty-seven   81   78   80   76   87

2   **Find these numbers on the word search. They are written across → and down ↓.**

20   60

30   70

40   80

50   90

T	W	E	N	T	Y	E	F
N	S	I	X	T	Y	F	I
I	Y	G	N	H	V	O	F
N	E	H	E	Y	I	R	T
E	S	T	H	I	R	T	Y
T	R	Y	M	L	F	Y	E
Y	S	E	V	E	N	T	Y

Addition and subtraction

This **number trio** can make 4 addition and subtraction facts.

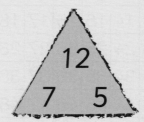

$7 + 5 = 12$ $12 - 7 = 5$

$5 + 7 = 12$ $12 - 5 = 7$

1 Fill in the addition and subtraction facts for these.

a

$5 + \boxed{} = \boxed{}$

$\boxed{} + 5 = \boxed{}$

$\boxed{} - 5 = \boxed{}$

$\boxed{} - \boxed{} = 5$

b

$\boxed{} + \boxed{} = 15$

$\boxed{} + 6 = 15$

$15 - \boxed{} = \boxed{}$

$15 - \boxed{} = \boxed{}$

c

$9 + \boxed{} = \boxed{}$

$\boxed{} + 9 = \boxed{}$

$\boxed{} - \boxed{} = 9$

$\boxed{} - 9 = \boxed{}$

2 Choose 8 different numbers from the line below to complete these facts.

$4 + \boxed{} = 9$

$7 - 5 = \boxed{}$

$8 - \boxed{} = 1$

$\boxed{} + \boxed{} = 11$

$12 - \boxed{} = 8$

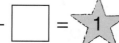
$\boxed{} + 3 = \boxed{}$

Counting patterns

Practise **counting on** and **back** in steps of 2, 5 and 10.

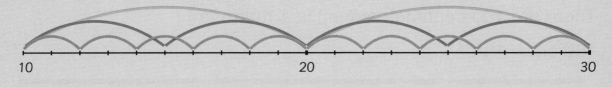

1 Continue each of these counting patterns to 100. Mark them on the 100 square like this:

2 4 6 8 10 12 → 100

5 10 15 20 25 → 100

10 20 30 40 50 → 100

1	2	3	4	5	6	7	8	9	10
11	12	13	14	15	16	17	18	19	20
21	22	23	24	25	26	27	28	29	30
31	32	33	34	35	36	37	38	39	40
41	42	43	44	45	46	47	48	49	50
51	52	53	54	55	56	57	58	59	60
61	62	63	64	65	66	67	68	69	70
71	72	73	74	75	76	77	78	79	80
81	82	83	84	85	86	87	88	89	90
91	92	93	94	95	96	97	98	99	100

2 Count in 5s and fill in the next 4 numbers.

a   4   9

b   22   27

c  43   48

Now count in 10s and fill in the next 4 numbers.

d   8   18

e   27   37

f   39   49

Measuring length

We measure lengths using **centimetres** and **metres**.

There are 100 centimetres (cm) in 1 metre (m).

100 cm = 1 m

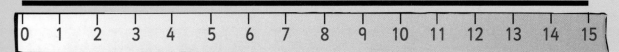

This line shows 15 cm.

1 Use a ruler to measure each of these lengths in centimetres.

a _____ [ ] cm

b _____ [ ] cm

c _____ [ ] cm

d ____ [ ] cm

e _____ [ ] cm

f _____ [ ] cm

> Try estimating the length before you measure.

2 Draw lines to join these objects to the most likely length.

about 1 metre

about 2 metres

about 10 centimetres

more than 2 metres

about 50 cm

Finding totals

When you add together 3 or more numbers, try **starting** with the **largest number**.

Here's how to total 4, 3 and 8:

$$8 + 4 = 12$$
$$12 + 3 = 15$$

You could look for pairs that are easy to total.

Here's how to total 6, 5 and 4:

$$6 + 4 = 10$$
$$10 + 5 = 15$$

1 **Fill in the totals for these sets of additions.**

a (6 2 8) → ☐   d (9 1 8) → ☐   g (8 4 6) → ☐

b (5 2 9) → ☐   e (7 3 4) → ☐   h (3 3 8) → ☐

c (7 2 3) → ☐   f (5 9 5) → ☐   i (4 6 3) → ☐

2 **Make these totals in different ways.**

a 4 + ☐ + ☐

☐ + ☐ + 5

☐ + 6 + ☐

13

☐ + 3 + ☐

8 + ☐ + ☐

☐ + ☐ + 1

b ☐ + ☐ + 9

☐ + 6 + ☐

7 + ☐ + ☐

18

4 + ☐ + ☐

☐ + 8 + ☐

☐ + ☐ + 5

Odd and even numbers

Even numbers always end in

2 4 6 8 0

36
is an even number.

Odd numbers always end in

1 3 5 7 9

63
is an odd number.

1 Write the next **even** number.

Write the next **odd** number.

a 22 → ☐

b 38 → ☐

c 46 → ☐

d 60 → ☐

e 54 → ☐

f 35 → ☐

g 57 → ☐

h 29 → ☐

i 87 → ☐

j 91 → ☐

2 Colour **purple** the even number trail. Start at the IN gate.

OUT

19	24	32	48	85	33	34	26	18	70	96	73	34	26	14
23	6	61	16	51	27	58	35	43	19	34	85	58	21	43
42	30	25	40	10	7	94	65	24	46	52	17	92	80	19
85	27	41	93	28	43	62	97	12	21	33	29	31	52	21
17	35	43	8	32	76	44	81	16	54	36	28	56	74	45

IN

How many stars have you collected? ☐

3-D shapes

A 3-D shape is a **solid shape**.

square face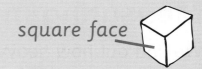

Learn the names of these shapes. Look at the faces.

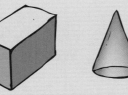 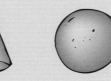

cube   cuboid   cone   sphere   cylinder   pyramid

1 Draw lines to join each shape to its correct name.

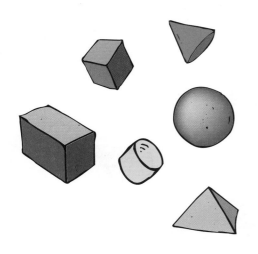

sphere

cylinder

cone

cuboid

pyramid

cube

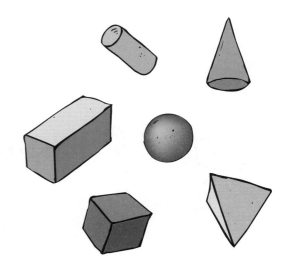

2 Fill in the number of faces for each of these shapes.

a   ☐ square faces

☐ rectangle faces

b   ☐ square faces

c  ☐ square faces

☐ triangle faces

d ☐ circle faces

and a curved face

Measuring mass

We find out how heavy something is by finding its **weight** or **mass**.

There are 1000 grams (g) in 1 kilogram (kg).

1000 g = 1 kg

Find something that weighs about 1 kg.

1 **Join these to the most likely weight.**

2 **Write down the weight on the scales to the nearest kilogram.**

a   b   c   d

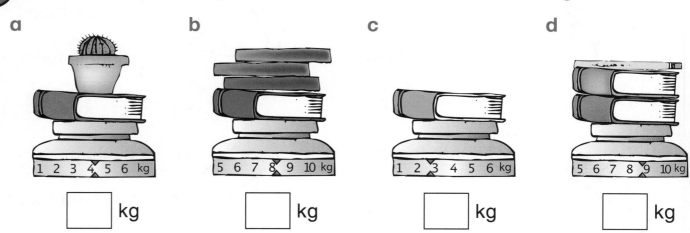

◻ kg   ◻ kg   ◻ kg   ◻ kg

Breaking up numbers

The numbers between **10** and **99** all have **two digits**.

$$57 \rightarrow 50 + 7$$

5 tens   7 ones

1 Fill in the missing numbers.

a 34 → 30 + ☐

b 51 → ☐ + 1

c 47 → 40 + ☐

d 65 → ☐ + 5

e 83 → 80 + ☐

f 42 → ☐ + 2

g 29 → 20 + ☐

h 76 → ☐ + 6

i 59 → 50 + ☐

2 Draw lines to join the matching pairs.

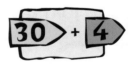

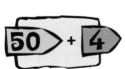 50 + 4

34

53

35

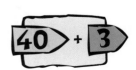 40 + 3

Reading the time

We count the minutes around a clock face in 5s. There are 60 minutes in one hour.

These clocks show **quarter past eight**.

 **8:15**

15 minutes have gone past 8 o'clock.

These clocks show **quarter to five**.

 **4:45**

45 minutes have gone past 4 o'clock.

1 Draw lines to join the clocks showing the same time.

a   b   c   d   e   f   g

 **11:30**   **3:10**   **1:15**   **12:45**   **6:35**   **4:15**   **7:55**

2 Write the number of minutes between each of these times.

a ☐ minutes

b **10:45** **11:00** ☐ minutes

c  ☐ minutes

d **3:15** **3:45** ☐ minutes

Multiplying

Counting in equal groups is also called **multiplying**.

The multiplication sign is ×.

3 + 3 + 3 + 3 = 12

4 + 4 + 4 = 12

3 multiplied by 4 is 12

4 multiplied by 3 is 12

3 × 4 = 12

4 × 3 = 12

These both give the same answer.

1 Write the answers to these facts.

a   2 + 2 + 2 = ☐

2 × 3 = ☐

d  4 + 4 = ☐

4 × 2 = ☐

b ●●●●●
   ●●●●● 5 + 5 = ☐

5 × 2 = ☐

e   3 + 3 + 3 = ☐

3 × 3 = ☐

c   3 + 3 + 3 + 3 + 3 = ☐

3 × 5 = ☐

f 4 + 4 + 4 + 4 = ☐

4 × 4 = ☐

2 Draw **2** spots on each hat.
Then write the answer.

Draw **3** spots on each hat.
Then write the answer.

a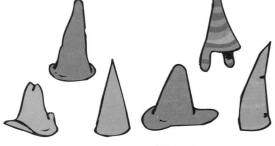

2 × 6 = ☐

b

3 × 6 = ☐

Symmetrical shapes

Shapes are **symmetrical** if they are the same either side of a **mirror line**.

The mirror line is called the **line of symmetry**.

1 Draw a line of symmetry on each of these shapes.

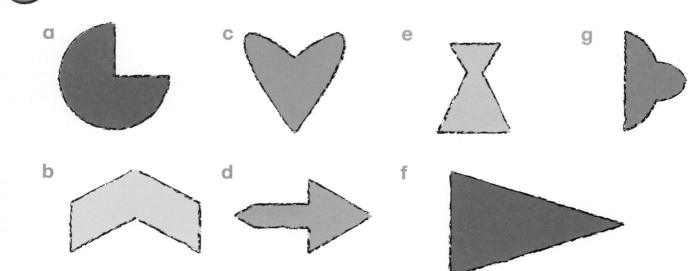

a

c

e

g

b

d

f

2 Complete this to make a symmetrical shape. Then colour it to make a symmetrical pattern.

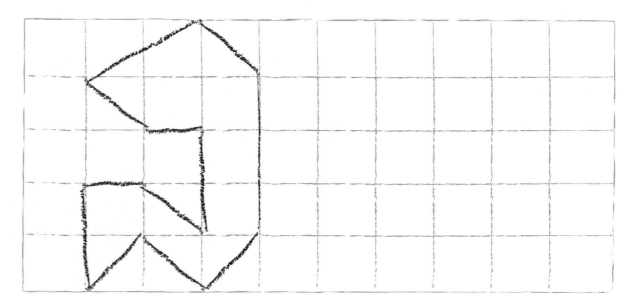

Comparing and ordering numbers

When you put **2-digit** numbers in order, look at the **tens and then the ones** digit.

52 is larger than 38 because 5 tens is more than 3 tens.

> means 'is greater than'
33 > 16
33 is greater than 16

< means 'is less than'
74 < 82
74 is less than 82

1 Write > or < in each box so the statements are correct.

a 76 ☐ 83

b 57 ☐ 48

c 34 ☐ 62

d 19 ☐ 51

e 83 ☐ 65

f 78 ☐ 44

g 69 ☐ 81

h 23 ☐ 45

i 98 ☐ 83

2 Write these sets in order, starting with the smallest amount.

a  ☐ p ☐ p ☐ p ☐ p ☐ p

58p 39p 85p 61p 42p

b 73 kg 69 kg 37 kg 39 kg 76 kg ☐ kg ☐ kg ☐ kg ☐ kg ☐ kg

c 32 cm 23 cm 80 cm 38 cm 28 cm ☐ cm ☐ cm ☐ cm ☐ cm ☐ cm

d £53 £62 £29 £65 £35 £☐ £☐ £☐ £☐ £☐

Dividing

Dividing a number of objects can be shown by grouping them.

The division sign is ÷

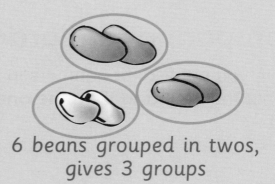

6 beans grouped in twos, gives 3 groups

$6 \div 2 = 3$

---

1 Draw loops around these beans to group them. Write the answers.

a 8 grouped in 2s

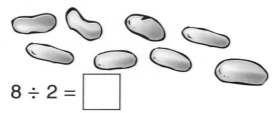

$8 \div 2 = \boxed{}$

c 12 grouped in 3s

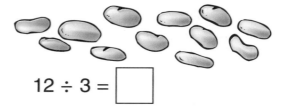

$12 \div 3 = \boxed{}$

b 9 grouped in 3s

$9 \div 3 = \boxed{}$

d 10 grouped in 2s

$10 \div 2 = \boxed{}$

---

2 Use the cookies to help you complete these.

a

$15 \div 5 = \boxed{}$

c

$10 \div 2 = \boxed{}$

b

$15 \div 3 = \boxed{}$

d

$10 \div 5 = \boxed{}$

Reading graphs

Block graphs show information in a simple way.

Count the blocks carefully or read across for the amount.

A group of children threw
10 beanbags, trying to get them
into a bucket.

How many more beanbags did
Zoe get in than Fred? Answer = 3

1 A group of children tested how many pegs they could hold in one hand.

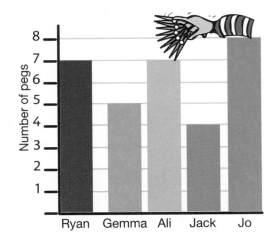

a Who held the most pegs?

b How many pegs did Gemma hold?

c Which 2 children held the same number of pegs?

d Who held the fewest pegs?

e How many more pegs did Jo hold than Jack?

2 Carry out your own peg test. Ask family and friends to hold as many pegs as they can in one hand. Record your results as a pictogram.

Name	Number of pegs

= 1 peg

Time

There are **12 months** or **52 weeks** in **a year**.

Try to learn the order of the months and the seasons. Think about the month and season you were born in.

spring

summer

autumn

winter

1 Complete the names of the months for each season.

spring

M __ __ c h

A __ r __ l

__ __ y

winter

D __ __ __ m b __ __

__ __ n u __ r __

F __ __ r __ __ __ y

summer

J __ __ e

__ __ __ y

A __ __ u __ __

autumn

S __ p __ __ __ __ __ r

__ __ t __ b __ __

N __ __ e __ b __ __

2 Complete these time facts.

a ☐ days in a week

b ☐ months in a year

c ☐ weeks in a year

d ☐ hours in a day

e ☐ minutes in an hour

f ☐ seconds in a minute

g ☐ days in a fortnight

h ☐ days in a weekend

i ☐ seasons in a year

j ☐ months in a season

2 times table

The numbers in the **2 times table** can be shown as a pattern.

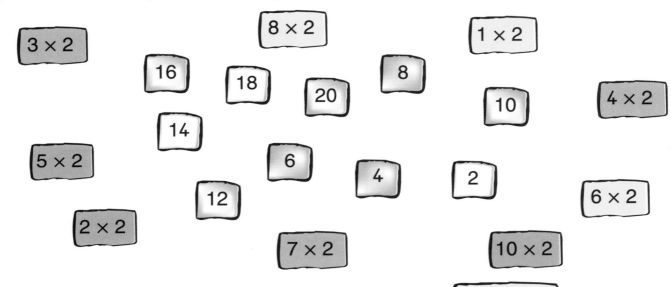

Try to learn the 2 times table by heart.

$$1 \times 2 = 2$$
$$2 \times 2 = 4$$

1 Draw lines to join the multiplications to the correct answers.

3 × 2

8 × 2

1 × 2

16

18

8

20

10

4 × 2

14

5 × 2

6

4

2

6 × 2

12

2 × 2

7 × 2

10 × 2

a Write a multiplication for the answer that is left.

2 Answer these questions as fast as you can. Ask someone to time you.

a 3 × 2 =

7 × 2 =

4 × 2 =

1 × 2 =

6 × 2 =

b 2 × 10 =

2 × 2 =

2 × 8 =

2 × 5 =

2 × 9 =

c 8 × 2 =

2 × 6 =

9 × 2 =

2 × 7 =

5 × 2 =

Half fractions

This chocolate bar is cut into **2 equal pieces**.

Each piece is **half ($\frac{1}{2}$)** of the whole bar.

There are 8 squares of chocolate.

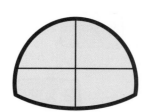

$\frac{1}{2}$ of 8 = 4

1 Colour $\frac{1}{2}$ of each shape.

a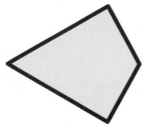

b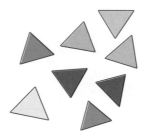

c

d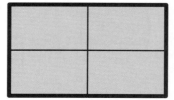

e

f

2 Circle $\frac{1}{2}$ of each set. Write the answer.

a 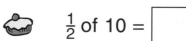 $\frac{1}{2}$ of 6 = ☐

b 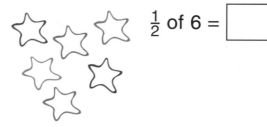 $\frac{1}{2}$ of 8 = ☐

c  $\frac{1}{2}$ of 10 = ☐

d $\frac{1}{2}$ of 4 = ☐

Measuring capacity

The **capacity** of a jug is how much **liquid** it holds.

1000 millilitres (ml) = 1 litre (l)

Fill a 1 litre jug so that you know how much a litre is.

---

1 Draw lines to join these things to the most likely amount.

  less than 1 litre   greater than 1 litre

---

2 Write down these amounts to the nearest litre.

a

☐ litres

c

☐ litres

e

☐ litres

b

☐ litres

d

☐ litres

f

☐ litres

Money

Practise finding totals of **coins** and giving **change**. When you give change, try counting up.

A cake costs 39p. Think about the change you will get from 50p.

Count on from 39p to 50p.

+1p   +10p

39p   40p   50p

The change is 11p.

1 Draw the 3 coins you would use to buy each of these.

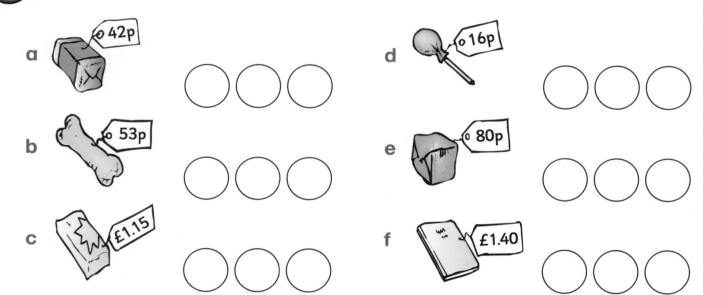

a 42p

b 53p

c £1.15

d 16p

e 80p

f £1.40

2 This is the change given from **50p**. How much did each cake cost?

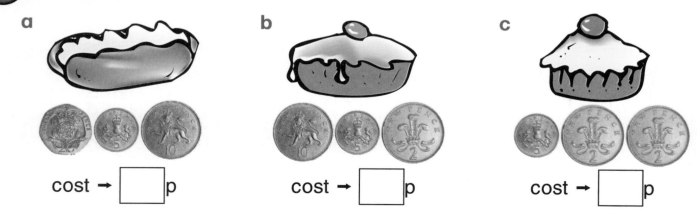

a

cost → ☐ p

b

cost → ☐ p

c

cost → ☐ p

Number sequences

When you are writing sequences of numbers, look at the **difference** between each number.

This sequence counts on in **steps of 2**.

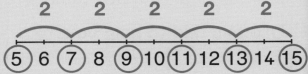

The difference between each number is 2.

This sequence counts on in **steps of 3**.

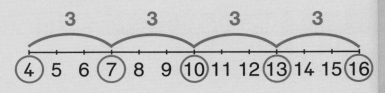

The difference between each number is 3.

1 Write the next 2 numbers in each sequence.

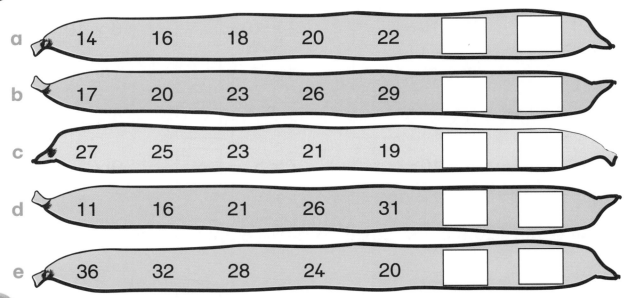

a 14   16   18   20   22   ☐ ☐

b 17   20   23   26   29   ☐ ☐

c 27   25   23   21   19   ☐ ☐

d 11   16   21   26   31   ☐ ☐

e 36   32   28   24   20   ☐ ☐

2 Write 3 sequences of your own. The number 20 must be in each sequence.

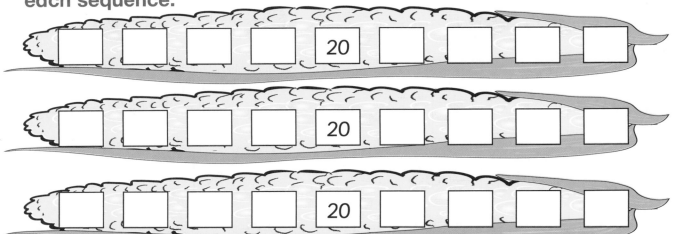

☐ ☐ ☐ ☐ 20 ☐ ☐ ☐ ☐

☐ ☐ ☐ ☐ 20 ☐ ☐ ☐ ☐

☐ ☐ ☐ ☐ 20 ☐ ☐ ☐ ☐

Multiplication facts

Try to learn the **2** times,
5 times and **10** times tables.

Use this grid to help you.

×	1	2	3	4	5	6	7	8	9	10
2	2	4	6	8	10	12	14	16	18	20
5	5	10	15	20	25	30	35	40	45	50
10	10	20	30	40	50	60	70	80	90	100

1 Cover the grid above. Now answer these questions as fast as you can. Check your answers, then try to beat your score.

a $3 \times 5 = \boxed{}$

$6 \times 2 = \boxed{}$

$4 \times 10 = \boxed{}$

$8 \times 2 = \boxed{}$

$4 \times 5 = \boxed{}$

b $4 \times 2 = \boxed{}$

$7 \times 10 = \boxed{}$

$9 \times 2 = \boxed{}$

$5 \times 5 = \boxed{}$

$3 \times 10 = \boxed{}$

c $2 \times 2 = \boxed{}$

$9 \times 10 = \boxed{}$

$6 \times 5 = \boxed{}$

$2 \times 10 = \boxed{}$

$7 \times 5 = \boxed{}$

d $5 \times 2 = \boxed{}$

$8 \times 10 = \boxed{}$

$10 \times 5 = \boxed{}$

$3 \times 2 = \boxed{}$

$9 \times 5 = \boxed{}$

2 Write the digits 1 to 9 in the boxes to make each multiplication correct.

$2 \times \boxed{} = \boxed{}$

$\boxed{} \times 5 = 20$

$\boxed{}0 \times \boxed{} = 80$

$\boxed{} \times \boxed{} = 35$

$\boxed{} \times \boxed{} = 18$

$\boxed{} \times \boxed{} = 40$

Quarter fractions

This cake is cut into **4 equal pieces**.

Each piece is **one quarter ($\frac{1}{4}$)** of the whole cake.

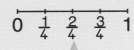

$\frac{2}{4}$ is the same as $\frac{1}{2}$

$\frac{1}{4}$ of 8 = 2

$\frac{3}{4}$ of 8 = 6

1 Colour $\frac{1}{4}$ of each shape.

a

c

e
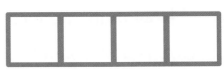

b

d
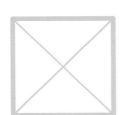

f

2 Colour $\frac{3}{4}$ of the ribbons on these badges. Make sure each pattern is different.

Problems

Read word problems carefully. Look for **key words** to help you.

add, total, sum, altogether, plus, increase

subtract, take away, difference, fewer, decrease

times, multiply, lots of, double, groups of

share, divide, group, halve

1 Answer these problems.

a Four friends share 20 pencils equally between them. How many pencils do they each have?

b A T-shirt costs £3.50. What change will there be from £5?

c Tom buys 2 boxes of eggs with 6 eggs in each. When he gets home he finds that 3 eggs are cracked. How many eggs are not cracked?

d When a tree was planted, it was 2 metres high. After 5 years it was 10 times as high. What height was it after 5 years?

e Entrance to a fête costs 40p for adults and 10p for children. What is the total cost for a family of 2 adults and 3 children?

2 Answer these 'think of a number' puzzles.

a I think of a number and then add 2. The answer is 7. What was my number?

b I think of a number and then take away 5. The answer is 6. What was my number?

c I think of a number and then halve it. The answer is 4. What was my number?

d I think of a number and then double it. The answer is 10. What was my number?

Finding the difference

To find the **difference** between 2 numbers, count on from the smaller number.

What is the difference between 19 and 23?

19   20   21   22   23   24   25 $23 - 19 = 4$

1 Write the difference in price between these pairs of items.

a

Difference: £ ⬚

c

Difference: £ ⬚

e

Difference: £ ⬚

b

Difference: £ ⬚

d

Difference: £ ⬚

f

Difference: £ ⬚

2 Draw lines to join pairs with a difference of 6.

56   68   62   75   83   94   74   88   81   77

Test 1 Read and write numbers to 100

Use these numbers to help you.

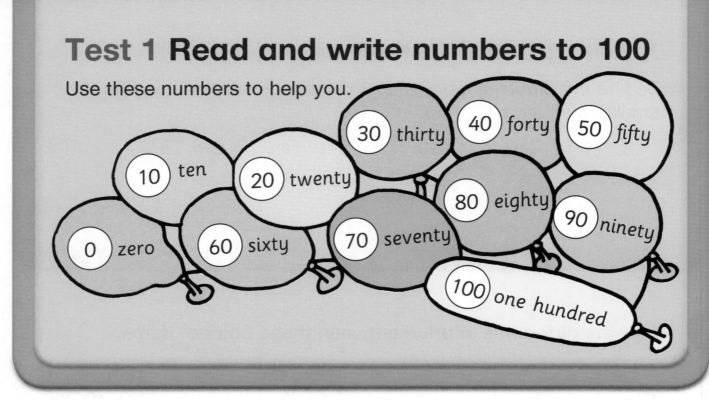

Write the numbers to match the words.

1. thirty-four

2. forty-six

3. twenty-eight

4. seventy-two

5. eighty-nine

Write these numbers as words.

6. 23 _____

7. 56 _____

8. 91 _____

9. 67 _____

10. 49 _____

Colour in your score

Test 2 Addition

We use a **number line** to help us **add on**.

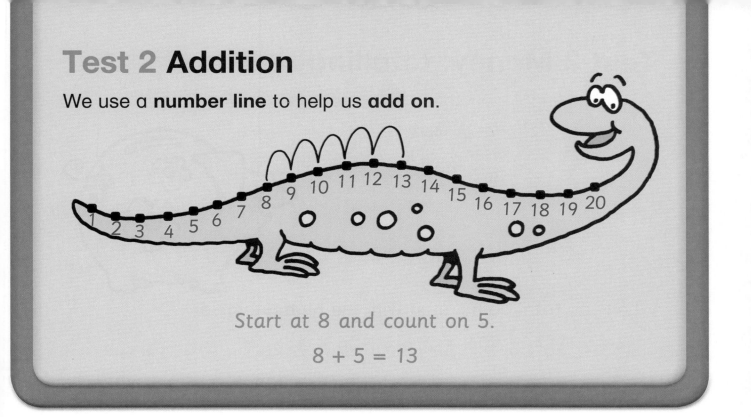

Start at 8 and count on 5.

$8 + 5 = 13$

Use the number line to help you work out the answers.

1. 6 + 5 =

2. 11 + 3 =

3. 8 + 6 =

4. 12 + 4 =

5. 9 + 5 =

6. 16 + 11 =

7. 70 + 9 =

8. 30 + 50 =

9. 54 + 4 =

10. 33 + 6 =

Colour in your score

33

Test 3 Money: totalling

When you **total coins**, start with the **highest** value.

50p + 20p + 10p + 5p = 85p

Total each set of coins.

1. (10p) (50p) (2p) ⇨ [62] p

2. (5p) (2p) (2p) (10p) ⇨ [39] p

3. (2p) (1p) (20p) (10p) ⇨ [33] p

4. (20p) (10p) (50p) (2p) ⇨ [82] p

5. (2p) (5p) (10p) (1p) ⇨ [1 8] p

6. (50p) (20p) (2p) (1p) ⇨ [ ] p

7. (20p) (20p) (2p) (10p) (2p) ⇨ [ ] p

8. (2p) (1p) (10p) (5p) (10p) ⇨ [ ] p

9. (50p) (20p) (5p) (10p) (1p) ⇨ [ ] p

10. (2p) (10p) (2p) (5p) (20p) ⇨ [ ] p

Colour in your score

34

Test 4 **2-D shapes**

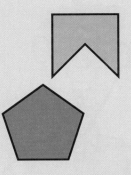
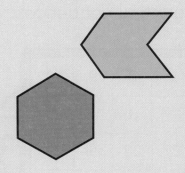
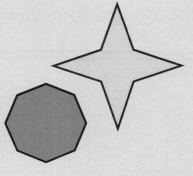

pentagons   hexagons   octagons

Answer these questions.

1. All triangles have ☐ sides.

2. All hexagons have ☐ sides.

3. All pentagons have ☐ sides.

4. All octagons have ☐ sides.

5. All quadrilaterals have ☐ sides.

Name these shapes.

6. _____

7. _____

8. _____

9. _____

10. _____

Colour in your score

35

Test 5 Counting sequences within 50

Use the grid to help with counting sequences.

1	2	3	4	5	6	7	8	9	10
11	12	13	14	15	16	17	18	19	20
21	22	23	24	25	26	27	28	29	30
31	32	33	34	35	36	37	38	39	40
41	42	43	44	45	46	47	48	49	50

Write the missing number in each sequence.

1. 24 25 26 ◯ 28 29

2. 35 36 37 38 ☐ 40

3. ☐ 19 20 21 22 23

4. 41 ☐ 43 44 45 46

5. 28 29 30 31 32 ◯

6. 43 42 41 ☐ 39 38

7. 29 28 ☐ 26 25 24

8. 18 ☐ 16 15 14 13

9. 47 46 45 44 ◯ 42

10. ☐ 39 38 37 36 35

Colour in your score

36

Test 6 Subtraction: finding differences

Counting in jumps can help to find the difference.

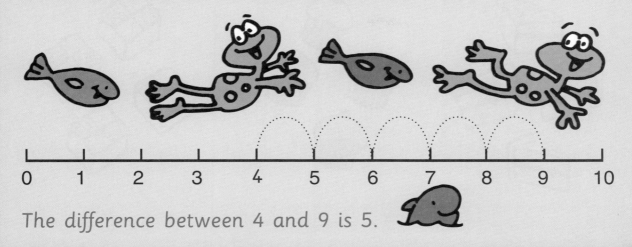

The difference between 4 and 9 is 5.

Write the differences between these pairs of numbers.

1.   ☐

6.   ☐

2.   ☐

7.   ☐

3.   ☐

8.   ☐

4.   ☐

9.   ☐

5.   ☐

10.   ☐

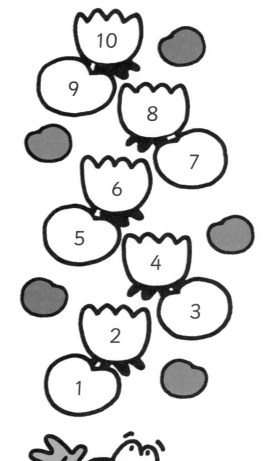

Colour in your score

Test 7 Multiplication: repeated addition

3 lots of 4 is 12

Write the answers.

1. 3 lots of 2 ⇨ [ ]

2. 2 lots of 4 ⇨ [ ]

3. 3 lots of 3 ⇨ [ ]

4. 2 lots of 5 ⇨ [ ]

5. 4 lots of 3 ⇨ [ ]

6. 2 lots of 2 ⇨ [ ]

7. 5 lots of 3 ⇨ [ ]

8. 3 lots of 5 ⇨ [ ]

9. 4 lots of 2 ⇨ [ ]

10. 2 lots of 3 ⇨ [ ]

Colour in your score

Test 8 Division: sharing

These sweets are shared equally.

15 sweets among 3 children ⟹ 5 each.

Write the answers.

1. 12 shared by 2 ⟹ ☐

2. 8 shared by 4 ⟹ ☐

3. 6 shared by 3 ⟹ ☐

4. 10 shared by 2 ⟹ ☐

5. 9 shared by 3 ⟹ ☐

6. 12 shared by 3 ⟹ ☐

7. 10 shared by 5 ⟹ ☐

8. 6 shared by 2 ⟹ ☐

9. 12 shared by 4 ⟹ ☐

10. 8 shared by 2 ⟹ ☐

Colour in your score

Test 9 Time (1)

Write the times for each clock.
Choose from these times.

| 1.15 | 3.30 | 4.45 | 8.00 | 2.30 |
| 8.45 | 3.15 | 7.30 | 9.00 | 4.15 |

1.

2.

3.

4.

5.

6.

7.

8.

9.

10.

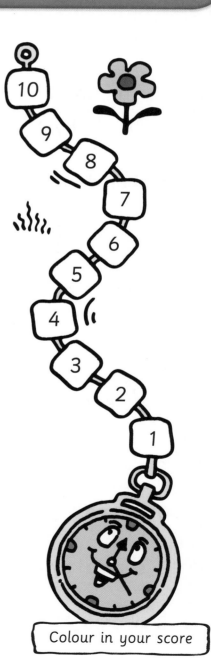

Colour in your score

Test 10 Data: block graphs

Colour this **graph** showing the favourite fruit of a group of children.

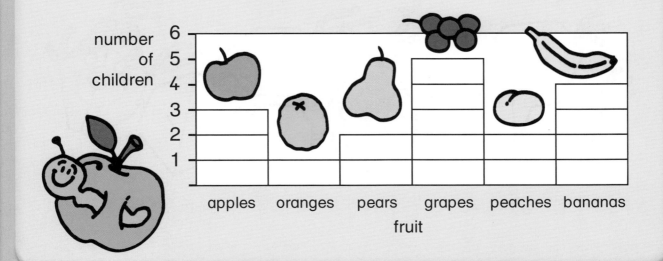

number of children

6
5
4
3
2
1

apples   oranges   pears   grapes   peaches   bananas

fruit

How many children chose:

1. oranges?

2. grapes?

3. bananas?

4. peaches?

5. Which fruit was the children's favourite?

6. Which fruit was chosen by 3 children?

7. How many more children chose grapes than peaches?

8. How many fewer children chose oranges than bananas?

9. How many children chose pears and peaches altogether?

10. How many children were there altogether?

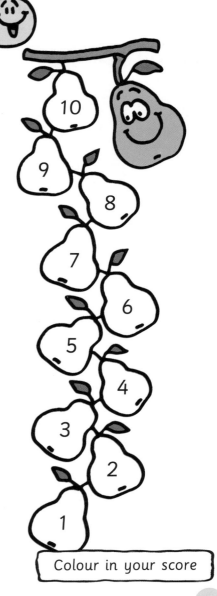

10
9
8
7
6
5
4
3
2
1

Colour in your score

Test 11 Breaking up numbers

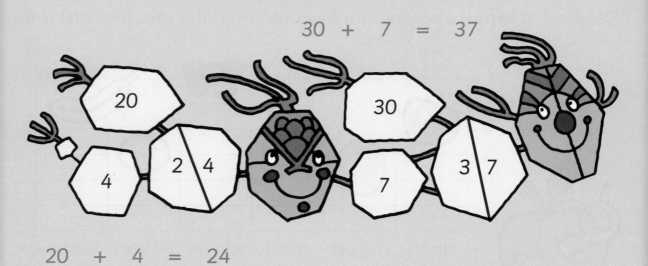

$$30 + 7 = 37$$

$$20 + 4 = 24$$

Write the missing numbers.

1. $43 = \boxed{} + 3$

2. $56 = 50 + \boxed{}$

3. $39 = 30 + \boxed{}$

4. $61 = \boxed{} + 1$

5. $27 = \boxed{} + 7$

6. $46 = 40 + \boxed{}$

7. $83 = \boxed{} + 3$

8. $74 = \boxed{} + 4$

9. $32 = 30 + \boxed{}$

10. $91 = \boxed{} + 1$

Colour in your score

42

Test 12 Subtraction facts

This is a **function machine** for changing numbers.

$$17 - 4 = 13$$

Write the missing numbers.

1. $18 - \boxed{} = 15$

2. $\boxed{} - 2 = 13$

3. $17 - 3 = \boxed{}$

4. $\boxed{} - 4 = 15$

5. $19 - \boxed{} = 16$

6. $26 - 2 = \boxed{}$

7. $\boxed{} - 3 = 27$

8. $26 - \boxed{} = 21$

9. $36 - \boxed{} = 31$

10. $\boxed{} - 4 = 43$

Colour in your score

Test 13 Money: giving change

When we work out **change** with **coins**,
we often **start** with the **smallest value**.

  65p

change: 35p

£1 is given for each toy. Write the change given.

1. 85p [ ] p

2. 70p [ ] p

3. 55p [ ] p

4. 60p [ ] p

5. 80p [ ] p

6. 45p [ ] p

7. 75p [ ] p

8. 89p [ ] p

9. 78p [ ] p

10. 67p [ ] p

10
9
8
7
6
5
4
3
2
1

Colour in your score

44

Test 14 3-D shapes

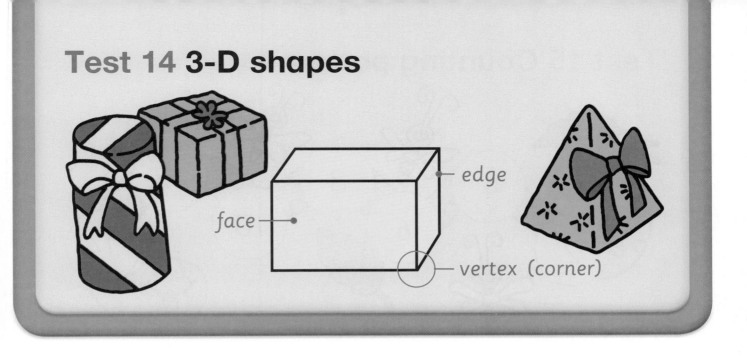

face · —— edge

vertex (corner)

Name these shapes.

1.

_____

2.

_____

3.

_____

4.

_____

5.

6.

How many faces have each of these shapes?

7.  ⬜ faces

8. ⬜ faces

9. ⬜ faces

10. ⬜ faces

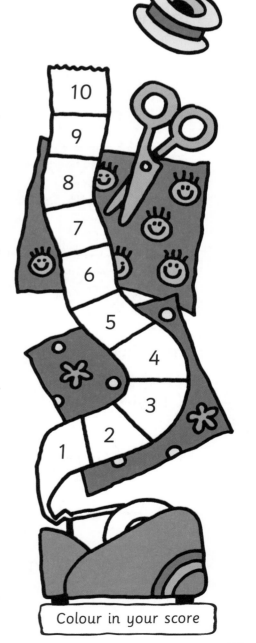

Colour in your score

45

Test 15 Counting patterns

4   8   12   6   2   10   14

Write the next number in the pattern.

1. 18 20 22 24 26 ◯

2. 34 36 38 40 42 ☐

3. 20 25 30 35 40 ◯

4. 15 18 21 24 27 ☐

5. 8 12 16 20 24 ◯

Write the missing number.

6. —14—☐—18—20—22—24—

7. —45—40—35—☐—25—20—

8. —9—12—☐—18—21—24—

9. —28—24—20—16—☐—8—

10. —☐—27—24—21—18—15—

Colour in your score

46

Test 16 Decade sums

Answer these questions.

1. 40 + 20 = ☐

2. 30 + 30 = ☐

3. 30 + 10 = ☐

4. 40 + 60 = ☐

5. 50 + 40 = ☐

6. 20 + 20 = ☐

The three corner numbers add up to 100.
Write the missing number.

7.
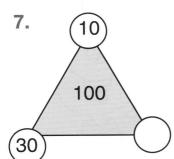
10 · 100 · 30 · ○

8.
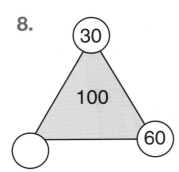
30 · 100 · ○ · 60

9.
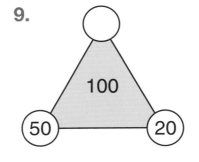
○ · 100 · 50 · 20

10.
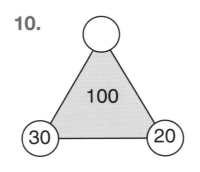
○ · 100 · 30 · 20

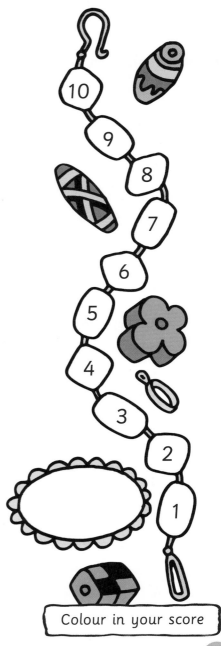

Colour in your score

47

Test 17 2 times table

You need to know your **2 times table**.

How quickly can you answer these?

1.   3 × 2 = ☐

2.   7 × 2 = ☐

3.   2 × 6 = ☐

4.   8 × 2 = ☐

5.   2 × 4 = ☐

6.   2 × 9 = ☐

7.   5 × 2 = ☐

8.   1 × 2 = ☐

9.   10 × 2 = ☐

10. 2 × 2 = ☐

Colour in your score

$\frac{1}{2}$ not $\frac{1}{2}$ $\frac{1}{4}$ not $\frac{1}{4}$

Colour $\frac{1}{2}$ of each shape.   **Colour $\frac{1}{4}$ of each shape.**

1.

2.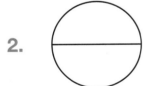

3.

4.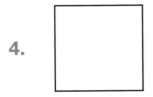

5.

6.

7.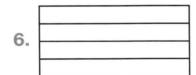

8.

9.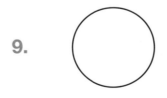

10.

Colour in your score

Test 19 Measures: length

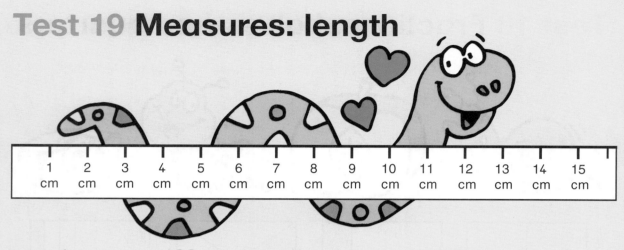

1 metre = 100 centimetres   1 m = 100 cm

Measure these lines.

1. _____ ☐ cm

2. _____ ☐ cm

3. _____ ☐ cm

4. _____ ☐ cm

5. _____ ☐ cm

Guess how long each worm is.

6. ☐ cm

7. ☐ cm

8. ☐ cm

9. ☐ cm

10. ☐ cm

Colour in your score

50

Test 20 Data: pictograms

This **pictogram** shows the pets owned by a group of children.

dogs	🐕 🐕 🐕 🐕 🐕
cats	🐱 🐱 🐱 🐱 🐱 🐱
rabbits	🐰 🐰 🐰
mice	🐭 🐭 🐭
fish	🐟 🐟 🐟 🐟

How many children have a pet:

1. dog

2. fish

3. mouse

4. rabbit

5. cat

6. How many more cats are there than fish ?

7. How many fewer rabbits are there than dogs?

8. How many mice and cats are there altogether?

9. How many fish and dogs are there altogether?

10. How many pets are there altogether?

Colour in your score

51

Test 21 Comparing and ordering numbers

Use this **number line** to help you **compare** and **order numbers**.

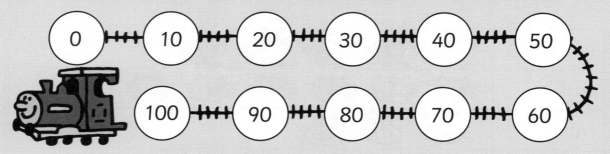

Remember: > means 'is greater than' < means 'is less than'

Write > or < in each box so the statements are correct.

1. 46 ☐ 61   4. 93 ☐ 39

2. 68 ☐ 83   5. 57 ☐ 54

3. 39 ☐ 41

Write the numbers in order starting with the smallest.

6. 18 34 27 41 ☐

7. 61 52 59 62 ☐

8. 38 41 52 37 ☐

9. 51 53 59 54 ☐

10. 72 69 64 70 ☐

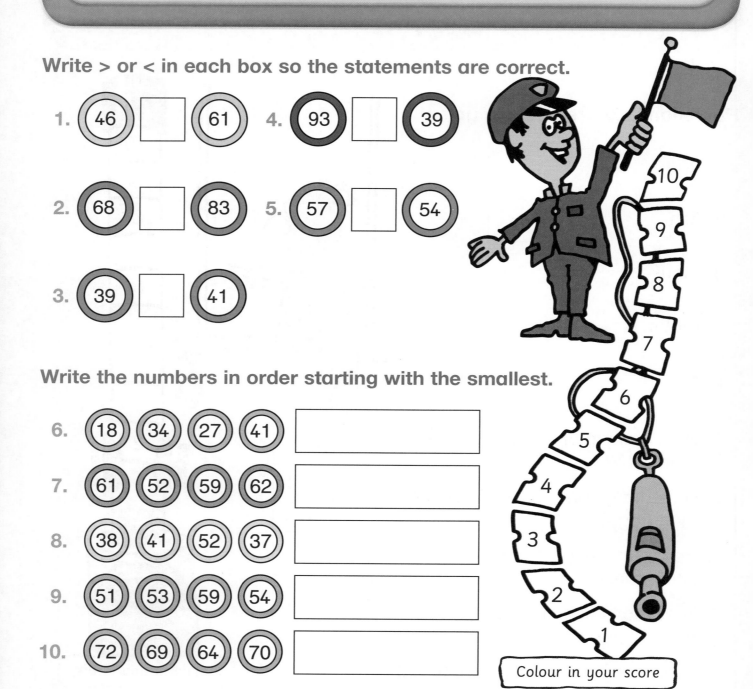

Colour in your score

52

Test 22 Addition and subtraction

This **number trio** makes **addition** and **subtraction** facts.

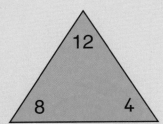

| 8 | + | 4 | = | 12 |
| 4 | + | 8 | = | 12 |

| 12 | – | 4 | = | 8 |
| 12 | – | 8 | = | 4 |

Write the addition and subtraction facts for each of these number trios.

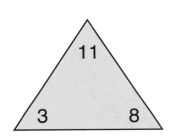

3 + 8 = 11

8 + 3 = 11

1. 11 – ☐ = 8

2. 11 – 8 = ☐

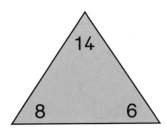

3. 8 + ☐ = 14

4. 6 + ☐ = ☐

5. ☐ – 6 = ☐

6. ☐ – 8 = ☐

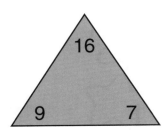

7. ☐ + 7 = ☐

8. ☐ + 9 = ☐

9. 16 – ☐ = ☐

10. ☐ – ☐ = 7

Colour in your score

53

Test 23 **Problems**

To work out a **missing number** use the other numbers to help you.

$$\boxed{} \quad + \quad 6 \quad = \quad 15$$

Something add 6 equals 15.

$$9 \quad + \quad 6 \quad = \quad 15$$

Write the missing numbers.

1. $\boxed{} \quad + \quad 3 \quad = \quad 11$

2. $6 \quad + \quad \boxed{} \quad = \quad 12$

3. $\boxed{} \quad + \quad 7 \quad = \quad 15$

4. $\boxed{} \quad + \quad 4 \quad = \quad 12$

5. $9 \quad + \quad 6 \quad = \quad \boxed{}$

6. $8 \quad + \quad \boxed{} \quad = \quad 16$

7. $4 \quad + \quad \boxed{} \quad = \quad 11$

8. $\boxed{} \quad + \quad 7 \quad = \quad 10$

9. $5 \quad + \quad 8 \quad = \quad \boxed{}$

10. $9 \quad + \quad \boxed{} \quad = \quad 18$

Colour in your score

10
9
8
7
6
5
4
3
2
1

Test 24 Shapes

These shapes have a line of **symmetry**.

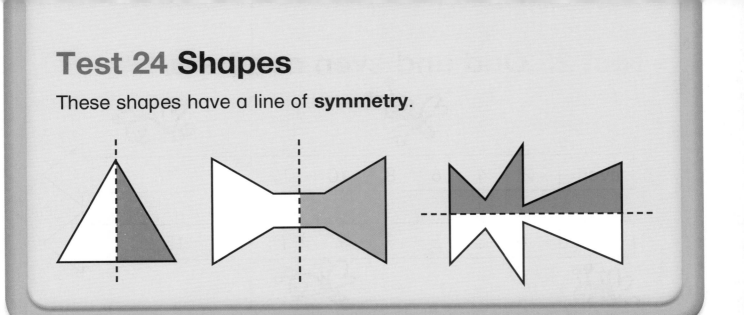

Draw the lines of symmetry on these shapes.

1.

2.

3.

4.

5.

Name these shapes.
Tick them if they are symmetrical.

6.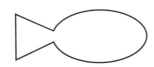

_____ ☐

7.

_____ ☐

8.

_____ ☐

9.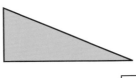

_____ ☐

10.

_____ ☐

Colour in your score

Test 25 Odd and even numbers

even	2	4	6	8	10	12	14	16

odd	1	3	5	7	9	11	13	15

Write the next even number.

1. 22 ☐

2. 28 ☐

3. 36 ☐

4. 44 ☐

5. 40 ☐

Write the next odd number.

6. 39 ☐

7. 41 ☐

8. 27 ☐

9. 35 ☐

10. 43 ☐

10
9
8
7
6
5
4
3
2
1

Colour in your score

Test 26 Money and place value

Do you know the shapes, values and sizes of these coins?

Write each of these totals.

1. (20p) (20p) (10p) (£1) ⇨ £ ☐ and ☐ p

2. (50p) (50p) (20p) (10p) ⇨ £ ☐ and ☐ p

3. (20p) (20p) (50p) (£1) ⇨ £ ☐ and ☐ p

4. (£1) (£1) (20p) (10p) ⇨ £ ☐ and ☐ p

5. (£1) (50p) (20p) (10p) ⇨ £ ☐ and ☐ p

6. (£1) (£2) (20p) (10p) ⇨ £ ☐ and ☐ p

7. (10p) (20p) (20p) (£2) ⇨ £ ☐ and ☐ p

8. (£2) (£2) (50p) (20p) ⇨ £ ☐ and ☐ p

9. (50p) (50p) (20p) (£2) ⇨ £ ☐ and ☐ p

10. (20p) (50p) (£1) (£1) ⇨ £ ☐ and ☐ p

| 10 |
| 9 |
| 8 |
| 7 |
| 6 |
| 5 |
| 4 |
| 3 |
| 2 |
| 1 |

Colour in your score

Test 27 10 times table

You need to know your **10 times table**.

How quickly can you answer these?

1. 4 × 10 =

2. 10 × 3 =

3. 7 × 10 =

4. 1 × 10 =

5. 5 × 10 =

6. 10 × 6 =

7. 10 × 2 =

8. 8 × 10 =

9. 10 × 10 =

10. 9 × 10 =

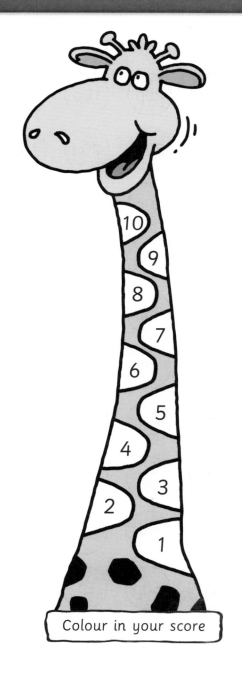

Colour in your score

Test 28 Fractions of quantities

$\frac{1}{3}$ of 6 = 2

$\frac{2}{3}$ of 6 = 4

$\frac{1}{4}$ of 8 = 2

$\frac{3}{4}$ of 8 = 6

Circle the fruit to help find the fraction of each quantity.

1.  $\frac{1}{3}$ of 6 = ☐

2. 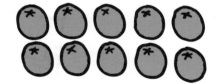 $\frac{1}{2}$ of 10 = ☐

3.  $\frac{1}{4}$ of 12 = ☐

Work out the answers.

4. $\frac{1}{2}$ of 8 = ☐

5. $\frac{1}{2}$ of 20 = ☐

6. $\frac{1}{2}$ of 14 = ☐

7. $\frac{1}{4}$ of 20 = ☐

8. $\frac{3}{4}$ of 12 = ☐

9. $\frac{1}{3}$ of 18 = ☐

10. $\frac{3}{4}$ of 4 = ☐

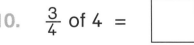

Colour in your score

Test 29 Time (2)

The **minute hand** tells you how many **minutes past the hour**.

Write the times.

1. _____ minutes past _____

2. _____ minutes past _____

3. _____ minutes past _____

4. _____ minutes past _____

5. _____ minutes past _____

Draw the hands to show the times.

6. 5.20

7. 8.35

8. 4.05

9. 3.55

10. 6.50

Colour in your score

60

Test 30 Data: tables

This **table** shows the colours of children's tops.

	Joe	Daniel	Becky	Gemma	Vijay	Sam	Jody	Sarah
blue	✓		✓		✓	✓		
black	✓	✓		✓	✓		✓	✓
green			✓					✓
red			✓			✓	✓	
yellow			✓			✓	✓	
white	✓	✓	✓				✓	✓

Look at the table and answer these questions.

1. Who has the most colours in their top? _____

2. Who has a black and white top? _____

3. What colours are in Sam's top? _____

4. Who has green in their top? _____

5. Who has no black in their top? _____

6. How many have white in their top? _____

7. How many have no blue in their top? _____

8. How many have 3 colours in their top? _____

9. Who has a top that is just one colour? _____

10. Who has no black or white in their top? _____

Colour in your score

ANSWERS

Page 2
1. a fifteen e 14
   b eighteen f 19
   c eleven g 12
   d seventeen h 16
2. a thirteen d seventeen
   b twelve e fourteen
   c eighteen f nineteen
   The hidden number is 11

Page 3
1. a 29, 30, 31, 33, 35, 36
   b 40, 41, 42, 45, 46, 47
   c 31, 30, 28, 25, 24
   d 50, 49, 47, 46, 42, 41
   e 17, 18, 19, 21, 23, 25
2. a

	5				
14	15		17		
24	25	26	27	28	29
	35	36	37	38	
	45	46			

b

22	23		25	26
32	33	34	35	36
42		44	45	

c

6	7	8		10
		18	19	20
		28	29	30
37	38	39	40	
		49	50	

Page 4
1. a 9   e 12   i 11
   b 12   f 14   j 13
   c 12   g 13   k 13
   d 9   h 15   l 14
2. a 42   e 46   i 43
   b 50   f 47   j 49
   c 40   g 41
   d 48   h 44
   45 is the star coloured in.

Page 5
1.
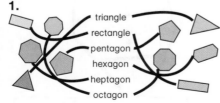
triangle, rectangle, pentagon, hexagon, heptagon, octagon
2. Check your child's colouring is accurate.

Page 6
1. a 7   c 5   e 12
   b 8   d 9   f 11
2. a 18 – 12, 30 – 24, 42 – 36, 24 – 18, 19 – 13
   b 24 – 17, 21 – 14, 39 – 32, 47 – 40, 23 – 16

Page 7
1. a 38   c 79   e 87
   b 54   d 62
2.

T	W	E	N	T	Y	E	F
N	S	I	X	T	Y	F	I
I	Y	G	N	H	V	O	F
N	E	H	E	Y	I	R	T
E	S	T	H	I	R	T	Y
T	R	Y	M	L	F	Y	E
Y	S	E	V	E	N	T	Y

Page 8
1. a 5 + 8 = 13   13 – 5 = 8
     8 + 5 = 13   13 – 8 = 5
   b 6 + 9 = 15   15 – 9 = 6
     9 + 6 = 15   15 – 6 = 9
   c 9 + 8 = 17   17 – 8 = 9
     8 + 9 = 17   17 – 9 = 8
2. 4 + 5 = 9   7 – 5 = 2
   8 – 7 = 1   8 + 3 = 11
   12 – 4 = 8   6 + 3 = 9

Page 9
1.

1	2	3	4	5	6	7	8	9	10
11	12	13	14	15	16	17	18	19	20
21	22	23	24	25	26	27	28	29	30
31	32	33	34	35	36	37	38	39	40
41	42	43	44	45	46	47	48	49	50
51	52	53	54	55	56	57	58	59	60
61	62	63	64	65	66	67	68	69	70
71	72	73	74	75	76	77	78	79	80
81	82	83	84	85	86	87	88	89	90
91	92	93	94	95	96	97	98	99	100

2. a 14, 19, 24, 29
   b 32, 37, 42, 47
   c 53, 58, 63, 68
   d 28, 38, 48, 58,
   e 47, 57, 67, 77
   f 59, 69, 79, 89

Page 10
1. a 5 cm   c 8 cm   e 10 cm
   b 6 cm   d 2 cm   f 11 cm
2. about 1 metre – child
   about 2 metres – door
   about 10 cm – pencil
   more than 2 metres – wall
   about 50 cm – book

Page 11
1. a 16   d 18   g 18
   b 16   e 14   h 14
   c 12   f 19   i 13
2. a There are many possible solutions, check your child's additions total 13.
   b There are many possible solutions, check your child's additions total 18.

Page 12
1. a 24   e 56   i 89
   b 40   f 37   j 93
   c 48   g 59
   d 62   h 31
2.

19	24	32	48	85	33	34	26	18	70	96	73	34	26	14
23	6	61	16	51	27	58	35	43	19	34	85	58	21	43
42	30	25	40	10	7	94	65	24	46	52	17	92	80	19
85	27	41	93	28	43	62	97	12	21	33	29	31	52	21
17	35	43	8	32	76	44	81	16	54	36	28	56	74	45

10 stars were collected.

Page 13
1.
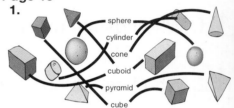
sphere, cylinder, cone, cuboid, pyramid, cube
2. a 2 square faces, 4 rectangle faces
   b 6 square faces
   c 1 square face, 4 triangle faces
   d 2 circle faces and a curved face

Page 14
1. Less than 1 kg – biscuits, grapes, slipper, crisps
   More than 1 kg – dog, potatoes, multi-pack of beans, encyclopedia
2. a 4 kg b 8 kg c 3 kg d 9 kg

Page 15
1. a 4   d 60   g 9
   b 50   e 3   h 70
   c 7   f 40   i 9
2.
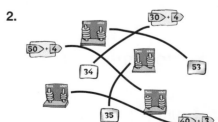

Page 16
1. a 1:15   d 7:55   g 4:15
   b 6:35   e 12:45
   c 11:30 f 3:10

2. a 30 minutes
   b 15 minutes
   c 45 minutes
   d 30 minutes

Page 17

1. a 6, 6   **d** 8, 8
   b 10, 10   **e** 9, 9
   c 15, 15   **f** 16, 16

2. a 12   **b** 18

Page 18

1. a c e g
   b d f

2.

Page 19

1. a 76 < 83   **f** 78 > 44
   b 57 > 48   **g** 69 < 81
   c 34 < 62   **h** 23 < 45
   d 19 < 51   **i** 98 > 83
   e 83 > 65

2. a 39p, 42p, 58p, 61p, 85p
   b 37 kg, 39 kg, 69 kg, 73 kg, 76 kg
   c 23 cm, 28 cm, 32 cm, 38 cm, 80 cm
   d £29, £35, £53, £62, £65

Page 20

1. a 4 **b** 3 **c** 4 **d** 5

2. a 3 **b** 5 **c** 5 **d** 2

Page 21

1. a Jo   **d** Jack
   b 5   **e** 4
   c Ali and Ryan

2. Check your child's graph is accurate.

Page 22

1. Spring: March, April, May
   Summer: June, July, August
   Autumn: September, October, November
   Winter: December, January, February

2. a 7   **e** 60   **h** 2
   b 12 **f** 60   **i** 4
   c 52 **g** 14   **j** 3
   d 24

Page 23

1. 3 × 2 → 6   4 × 2 → 8
   5 × 2 → 10   6 × 2 → 12
   2 × 2 → 4   10 × 2 → 20
   8 × 2 → 16   7 × 2 → 14
   1 × 2 → 2
   a 9 × 2 → 18

2. a 6, 14, 8, 2, 12
   b 20, 4, 16, 10, 18
   c 16, 12, 18, 14, 10

Page 24

1. Check your child has halved each shape accurately and coloured one-half. There is more than one solution to some of the shapes.

2. a 3 **b** 4 **c** 5 **d** 2

Page 25

1. Less than 1 litre – glass of squash, cup of tea, medicine bottle, soup bowl
   Greater than 1 litre – bottle of drink, fish tank, washing-up bowl, bucket

2. a 7 litres   **d** 4 litres
   b 9 litres   **e** 2 litres
   c 6 litres   **f** 8 litres

Page 26

1. a 20p, 20p, 2p
   b 50p, 2p, 1p
   c £1, 10p, 5p
   d 10p, 5p, 1p
   e 50p, 20p, 10p
   f £1, 20p, 20p

2. a 15p   **b** 33p   **c** 41p

Page 27

1. a 24, 26   **d** 36, 41
   b 32, 35   **e** 16, 12
   c 17, 15

2. Ask your child what the difference is between the numbers in each sequence and check the numbers are correct.

Page 28

1. a 15, 12, 40, 16, 20
   b 8, 70, 18, 25, 30
   c 4, 90, 30, 20, 35
   d 10, 80, 50, 6, 45

2. 2 × 1 = 2, 2 × 2 = 4,
    2 × 3 = 6 or 2 × 4 = 8
   4 × 5 = 20
   10 × 8 = 80, 20 × 4 = 80,
    40 × 2 = 80 or 80 × 1 = 80
   7 × 5 = 35 or 5 × 7 = 35
   2 × 9 = 18, 9 × 2 = 18,
    3 × 6 = 18 or 6 × 3 = 18
   5 × 8 = 40 or 8 × 5 = 40

Page 29

1. Check your child has divided each shape accurately into four parts and coloured one-quarter. There is more than one solution to some of the shapes.

2. There are many solutions. Check your child has coloured 6 squares on each badge.

Page 30

1. a 5 pencils   **d** 20m
   b £1.50   **e** £1.10
   c 9 eggs

2. a 5   **c** 8
   b 11   **d** 5

Page 31

1. a £5   **c** £5   **e** £4
   b £8   **d** £5   **f** £6

2.

Page 32

1. 34
2. 46
3. 28
4. 72
5. 89
6. twenty-three
7. fifty-six
8. ninety-one
9. sixty-seven
10. forty-nine

Page 33

1. 11   **6.** 27
2. 14   **7.** 79
3. 14   **8.** 80
4. 16   **9.** 58
5. 14   **10.** 39

Page 34

1. 62p   **6.** 73p
2. 19p   **7.** 54p
3. 33p   **8.** 28p
4. 82p   **9.** 86p
5. 18p   **10.** 39p

Page 35

1. 3
2. 6
3. 5
4. 8
5. 4
6. quadrilateral/square
7. pentagon
8. triangle
9. hexagon
10. rectangle/quadrilateral

Page 36

1. 27   **6.** 40
2. 39   **7.** 27
3. 18   **8.** 17
4. 42   **9.** 43
5. 33   **10.** 40

Page 37

1. 3   **6.** 5
2. 6   **7.** 3
3. 5   **8.** 7
4. 7   **9.** 30
5. 5   **10.** 5

Page 38

1. 6   **6.** 4
2. 8   **7.** 15
3. 9   **8.** 15
4. 10   **9.** 8
5. 12   **10.** 6

Page 39
1. 6
2. 2
3. 2
4. 5
5. 3
6. 4
7. 2
8. 3
9. 3
10. 4

Page 40
1. 9.00
2. 7.30
3. 4.15
4. 3.30
5. 8.00
6. 2.30
7. 8.45
8. 1.15
9. 4.45
10. 3.15

Page 41
1. 1
2. 5
3. 4
4. 2
5. grapes
6. apples
7. 3
8. 3
9. 4
10. 17

Page 42
1. 40
2. 6
3. 9
4. 60
5. 20
6. 6
7. 80
8. 70
9. 2
10. 90

Page 43
1. 3
2. 15
3. 14
4. 19
5. 3
6. 24
7. 30
8. 5
9. 5
10. 47

Page 44
1. 15p
2. 30p
3. 45p
4. 40p
5. 20p
6. 55p
7. 25p
8. 11p
9. 22p
10. 33p

Page 45
1. cylinder
2. cone
3. cuboid
4. sphere
5. square-based pyramid
6. cube
7. 5
8. 5
9. 6
10. 6

Page 46
1. 28
2. 44
3. 45
4. 30
5. 28
6. 16
7. 30
8. 15
9. 12
10. 30

Page 47
1. 60
2. 60
3. 40
4. 100
5. 90
6. 40
7. 60
8. 10
9. 30
10. 50

Page 48
1. 6
2. 14
3. 12
4. 16
5. 8
6. 18
7. 10
8. 2
9. 20
10. 4

Page 49
1.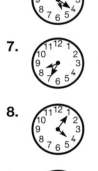
2.
3.
4.
5.
6.
7.
8.
9.
10.

Other solutions are possible.

Page 50
1. 4 cm
2. 2 cm
3. 6 cm
4. 7 cm
5. 8 cm
6. 4 cm
7. 5 cm
8. 7 cm
9. 8 cm
10. 6 cm

Page 51
1. 5
2. 4
3. 3
4. 3
5. 6
6. 2
7. 2
8. 9
9. 9
10. 21

Page 52
1. $46 < 61$
2. $68 < 83$
3. $39 < 41$
4. $93 > 39$
5. $57 > 54$
6. 18 27 34 41
7. 52 59 61 62
8. 37 38 41 52
9. 51 53 54 59
10. 64 69 70 72

Page 53
1. 3
2. 3
3. 6
4. $6 + 8 = 14$
5. $14 - 6 = 8$
6. $14 - 8 = 6$
7. $9 + 7 = 16$
8. $7 + 9 = 16$
9. $16 - 7 = 9$
10. $16 - 9 = 7$

Page 54
1. 8
2. 6
3. 8
4. 8
5. 15
6. 8
7. 7
8. 3
9. 13
10. 9

Page 55
1.
2.
3.
4.
5.
6. rectangle ✔
7. triangle
8. pentagon ✔
9. square ✔
10. hexagon ✔

Page 56
1. 24
2. 30
3. 38
4. 46
5. 42
6. 41
7. 43
8. 29
9. 37
10. 45

Page 57
1. £1 and 50p
2. £1 and 30p
3. £1 and 90p
4. £2 and 30p
5. £1 and 80p
6. £3 and 30p
7. £2 and 50p
8. £4 and 70p
9. £3 and 20p
10. £2 and 70p

Page 58
1. 40
2. 30
3. 70
4. 10
5. 50
6. 60
7. 20
8. 80
9. 100
10. 90

Page 59
1. 2
2. 5
3. 3
4. 4
5. 10
6. 7
7. 5
8. 9
9. 6
10. 3

Page 60
1. 10 minutes past 3
2. 40 minutes past 4
3. 45 minutes past 7
4. 50 minutes past 6
5. 20 minutes past 8

6.
7.
8.
9.
10.

Page 61
1. Becky
2. Daniel
3. blue, red, yellow
4. Becky and Sarah
5. Becky and Sam
6. 5
7. 4
8. 3
9. Gemma
10. Sam

English

Age 6-7

Contents

Activities

Quick Tests

Lynn Huggins-Cooper and Louis Fidge

Speaking and listening (1) – descriptions

It is important to be able to describe and explain things clearly – because then people understand what you mean!

1 **Describe your family to a friend.**

a Talk about how big your family is.

b Talk about where members of your family live.

c Talk about the jobs that the grown-ups do.

d Describe the things that your family likes to do.

e Draw a picture of your family in the box.

2 **Describe your favourite toy.**

a What is your favourite toy? _____

b Why is it your favourite? _____

c What does it look like? _____

d What does it do? _____

e How do you play with it? _____

f Draw a picture of the toy on a piece of paper to show when you are giving your explanation.

Speaking and listening (2) – explanations

It is important that you can describe and explain things clearly to other people – because then they will know exactly what you mean!

1 Do you have a pet? If not, find out about a pet you would like to own. Use the questions below to make some notes that explain to a grown-up how to take care of your pet.

a What equipment does your pet need?

b What does it eat?

c Where does it sleep?

d What exercise does it need?

e What toys can it play with?

f Draw a picture of your pet on a piece of paper that you can show when you are giving your explanation.

2 Imagine you are teaching a friend how to draw a picture of a house with a garden. Use the questions below to make notes about all the steps they need to follow.

a What equipment do they need?

b What do they draw first? Why?

c What comes next?

d How do they draw windows?

e What will go in the garden?

f Draw a picture of a house on a piece of paper to help you explain.

dge and ge

The letter strings *dge* and *ge* sound very similar – but they are spelt differently.

ba**dge**

bagga**ge**

1 Finish the words by writing *dge* or *ge*.

a bri_____

b ima_____

c villa_____

d nu_____

e sta_____

f ju_____

g ra_____

2 Choose the correct *dge* or *ge* word from the box to complete each sentence.

package lodge edge dodge fridge page fudge

a This _____ is delicious!

b We are staying in a wooden _____ for our holiday.

c I have finished the last _____ of my book.

d I got a _____ from Nana for my birthday.

e It fell off the _____ of the table.

f There is juice in the _____.

g I had to _____ the ball!

kn and *gn*

The letters *kn* and *gn* go at the start of a word. They both sound like *n* because the *k* or *g* is usually silent.

knee

gnome

---

1 Complete the words by adding the correct letters: *kn* or *gn*. Then draw a line to match each word to the correct picture.

a _____ot

b _____itting

c _____ome

d _____ife

e _____at

f _____ight

g _____uckle

---

2 Circle the correct spelling of each word and cross out the incorrect word. Write a sentence using each word.

a   knock gnock _____

b   knaw gnaw _____

c   know gnow _____

d   knash gnash _____

e   knu gnu _____

wr

Some words start with the letter pattern *wr*. When you say it out loud, you only hear the sound *r* because the *w* is silent.

 right

 **wr**ong

---

1 Complete the words by adding the letters *wr*. Then draw a line to match each word to the correct picture.

a _____eck

b _____ite

c _____ist

d _____inkle

e _____ap

f _____eath

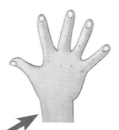

---

2 Find all the words that start with *wr*. Colour in the boxes, then write the words below.

wren	writer
ran	wrestler
rain	wriggle

rent	wrwng
ride	right
wrench	read

a _____

b _____

c _____

d _____

e _____

f _____

al and *il*

The word endings *al* and *il* sound very alike.

festiv**al**

pup**il**

1 Learn these spellings using the LOOK, COVER, WRITE, CHECK method.

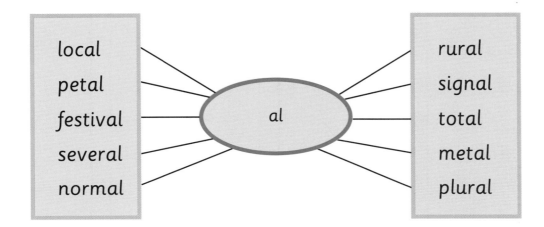

local		rural
petal		signal
festival	**al**	total
several		metal
normal		plural

2 Choose the correct ending by adding *al* or *il* to finish these words.

a pup_____

b tot_____

c civ_____

d penc_____

e met_____

f sign_____

g ev_____

h foss_____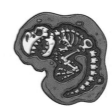

le and el

The *le* and *el* endings sound the same. The best way to know the difference is to learn the spellings. Remember to use the LOOK, COVER, WRITE, CHECK method.

*eas**el***   *bott**le***

1 Complete the words by adding *le* or *el*. Then choose three of the words and draw them in the boxes. Label your pictures.

a eag_____

b tunn_____

c map_____

d ang_____

e simp_____

f hot_____

g litt_____

h gigg_____

i chap_____

2 Underline the correct spelling of the word to complete each sentence. Cross out the incorrect spelling.

a I would like a **doubel double** choc chip ice cream, please.

b Just turn the **handel handle** and open the door.

c I saw a **squirrel squirrle** in the park.

d I went on a minibeast hunt and found a worm and a **beetle beetel**.

e I went to the **castel castle** and saw suits of armour.

f I washed my face with a **flannel flannle**.

g Please change the television **channle channel**.

Spelling *y* and *ies*

Here is a spelling rule for words that end in a consonant plus *y*. When you make the word plural (more than one), you change the *y* to *ies*.

baby

bab**ies**

1 Change these words to the plural.

a sky ➡ _____   e spy ➡ _____

b country ➡ _____   f jelly ➡ _____

c berry ➡ _____   g lady ➡ _____

d body ➡ _____   h study ➡ _____

2 Now change these plurals to the singular (one).

a parties ➡ _____   e enemies ➡ _____

b ponies ➡ _____   f cities ➡ _____

c puppies ➡ _____   g cherries ➡ _____

d stories ➡ _____   h flies ➡ _____

3 Label the pictures. Be careful – is it singular or plural?

_____   _____   _____

wh and *ch* blends

Lots of words start with the sounds *wh* and *ch*.

whiskers

cheese

 1 Write in the missing letters *wh* or *ch* to complete the words.

a

_____ale

d

_____air

g

_____illy

b

_____imp

e

_____iteboard

h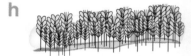

_____eat

c

_____isk

f

_____ips

i

_____istle

 2 Write a word beginning with *wh* to complete each question.

| When | Who | What | Why | Which | Where |

a _____ do you want to eat for lunch?

b _____ lives at number 7 Willow Street?

c _____ book do you prefer?

d _____ are you hiding behind the sofa?

Suffixes

Change the *y* to *i* before adding a suffix that starts with a consonant.

empty + ness = empt**i**ness

Drop the *e* at the end of a word before adding *ing, ed, er, est* and *y*.

wide + er = wid**er**

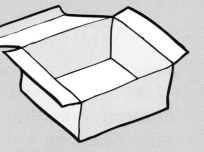

1 Add the suffix to each word.

a beauty + ful = _____

b lonely + ness = _____

c happy + ly = _____

2 Add the suffix to each word.

a hike + ing = _____

b shine + y = _____

c nice + est = _____

Look out for one syllable words that end with a single vowel followed by a single consonant. Double the last letter when you add ing, ed, er, est and y.

pat + ing = pat**t**ing

3 Add the suffix to these words.

a hum + ing = _____   d fat + er = _____

b drop + ed = _____   e run + y = _____

c sad + est = _____

Homophones

Homophones are words that sound the same even if they have a **different meaning** or **spelling**. Homophones may also be spelt the same, such as *bear* (animal) and *bear* (carry or put up with).

An example would be:

two *the number 2*
too *as well*
to *as in going to*

1 Draw a line to match the pairs of homophones. The first one is done for you.

a isle
b allowed
c ate
d I
e bear
f beech
g pair
h creek
i dear

pear
beach
deer
bare
I'll
eye
eight
creak
aloud

2 Cross out the homophone in each sentence that does not make sense.

a My auntie said I had **grown groan** since she last saw me.

b My **hare hair** is blonde.

c Can I come **two too**?

d A **herd heard** of sheep ran towards me.

e The **hole whole** class said hello.

f **Our Hour** cat likes fish.

g I **know no** your name.

h I **moan mown** if I have toothache.

Contractions

When you change a word to its shorter form, it is called a contraction. You use an **apostrophe** to show that one or more letters are missing.

it is ⟶ **it's**

1 Draw a line to match each pair of words to its contraction.

a can not   won't

b will not   isn't

c is not   I'm

d do not   can't

e I am   couldn't

f I would   I'll

g I will   don't

h could not   I'd

2 Choose the correct contraction from the box to complete each sentence.

| I'll | I'd | she's | It's | can't | don't | didn't |

a _____ like to fly to the moon.

b This sum is too hard. I _____ do it.

c When I get back from holiday _____ come and see you.

d Jessica lives next door and _____ my best friend.

e Come to DisneyWorld! _____ fantastic.

f Why _____ you come to school yesterday?

g I _____ like chips so I never eat them.

13

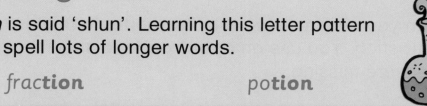

Words ending in *tion*

The ending *tion* is said 'shun'. Learning this letter pattern will help you to spell lots of longer words.

*frac***tion**   *po***tion**

1 **Fill in the missing letters.**

a audi __ __ __ __

b celebra __ __ __ __

c cau __ __ __ __

d collec __ __ __ __

e reflec __ __ __ __

f infec __ __ __ __

g rota __ __ __ __

h suc __ __ __ __

i hiberna __ __ __ __

j tradi __ __ __ __

2 **Choose a word from the box to complete each sentence so it makes sense.**

> tuition   station   fiction   exhibition   action   operation   auction

a I bought an antique vase at the _____.

b I have music _____ to help me play the violin.

c My gran went into hospital for an _____ to make her better.

d I caught a train at the _____.

e I like _____ films, where lots happens.

f I like reading _____ better than non-fiction.

g I saw some great art at the _____.

14

Possessive apostrophes

Possessive apostrophes show **ownership**. With singular words, you just add 's to show ownership.

If the word is plural and ends in s, the apostrophe comes after the s.

The cat**'s** whiskers.   The cat**s'** whiskers.

1 Add the possessive apostrophe in the correct place.
All these are singular.

a   The dog s paws were cold.

b   The girl s shoes were red.

c   The man s hat blew away!

d   The horse s mane is long.

e   The boy s lunch was tasty.

f   The woman s bag was heavy.

g   The baby s cry was really loud!

2 Now add the possessive apostrophes in these sentences.
All these are plural.

a   The dogs tails were all wagging.

b   All the girls books were about the seaside.

c   The birds beaks were pecking at the peanuts.

d   The puppies paws were so tiny!

e   All the cats bowls were empty.

f   The bats wings were flapping.

g   The boys coats were warm.

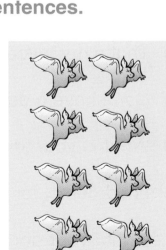

Statements, questions and exclamations

You get clues about whether sentences are statements, questions or exclamations. Statements have a **full stop** at the end, questions have a **question mark** and exclamations end with an **exclamation mark**.

. ? !

1 **Question or exclamation? Write Q or E in the box.**

a I love chocolate cake! ☐

b Is it time for tea yet? ☐

c What is your name? ☐

d That was loud! ☐

e I was really scared! ☐

f Would you like a biscuit? ☐

2 **Statement, question or exclamation? Write S, Q or E in the box.**

a I went shopping for new shoes. ☐

b That's my favourite show too! ☐

c Can I have a drink, please? ☐

d What is your favourite game? ☐

e I had cereal for breakfast. ☐

f Is that your dog? ☐

Commas in a list

When you make a list of things in a sentence, you should **separate** them with commas and put the word *and* between the last two things on the list.

I bought some eggs, potatoes, carrots, bananas and peppers.

1 Add commas in the correct places for each sentence.

a I like cats dogs and rabbits.

b I read books comics and newspapers.

c My favourite foods are cake toast and oranges.

d I collected shells stones and seaweed to decorate my sandcastle.

e Rainbows are red orange yellow green blue indigo and violet.

f It is cold so put on a hat scarf and gloves.

g I drink orange juice cola and milk.

h I saw tigers lions and hippos at the zoo.

2 Write sentences about these things. Include lists and don't forget the commas.

a animals _____

b games _____

c clothes _____

d toys _____

e vegetables _____

f plants _____

g bugs _____

h sports _____

Questions

Question marks show when a question has been asked.

Are we there yet**?**

Special question words also give us clues that questions are being asked:

Why Where

When What

Who Which How

1 Add the question marks to these sentences.

a What is your name___

b "Can I come too___" asked Mary.

c Why can't I___That's not fair!

d Would you like a sweet___

e Why not___ I want to!

f Do you like snakes___

g Do you want to come with me___ I don't mind.

h Can we go today___

i Who was that___

j Would anyone like some supper___

2 Choose a word from the box to make each question make sense. You can use the words more than once.

Why	Where	When	What	Who

a _____ said that?

b _____ are my keys?

c _____ is your name?

d _____ did you do that?

e _____ time is it?

f _____ is my pen?

g _____ can we go to the park?

h _____ would like to play with me

i _____ shall we go shopping?

j _____ would you like to drink?

Alphabetical order

Do you know the alphabet? Things are often organised in alphabetical order, so it is a good thing to know.

1) **Write these words in alphabetical order.**

a dog, cat, elephant

_____

b cake, pie, sandwich

_____

c pear, apple, orange

_____

d child, toddler, baby

_____

e plate, cup, spoon

_____

2) **Now write these names in alphabetical order.**

a Lucy, Ben, Peter

_____

b Selma, Nora, Jake

_____

c Rajan, Tom, Alex

_____

d Marissa, Charlie, Pat

_____

e Nicholas, Lena, Sophia

_____

Breaking words down

When you spell words, it is useful to break them into **smaller chunks**. This helps when you are reading too.

Drawing could be easily broken into *dr-aw-ing*.

1 Break these words into small chunks. Then learn to spell them.

a **snail**   breaks down into   _____-_____

b **writing**   breaks down into   _____-_____

c **hotel**   breaks down into   _____-_____

d **maybe**   breaks down into   _____-_____

e **donkey**   breaks down into   _____-_____

f **flowers**   breaks down into   _____-_____

g **carrot**   breaks down into   _____-_____

h **important**   breaks down into   _____-_____-_____

i **computer**   breaks down into   _____-_____-_____

2 Write the missing chunks of each word. Use the words in the box to help you.

| because |
| brother |
| sister |
| window |
| animal |
| should |
| jumping |
| another |

a sh-_____-ld

b br-_____-er

c be-cau-_____

d win-_____

e _____-i-mal

f _____-um-_____

g sis-_____

h an-_____-_____

Verbs

Verbs are the action words in a sentence. They tell you what is being done. Some people call them '**doing words**'.

Lick is a verb. It tells us what is being done.

1 Underline the verb in each sentence.

a The bird flew away.

b The girl laughed at her brothers.

c The mother ate a big slice of cake.

d The snake slid across the rocks.

e The lion roared.

f The two brothers shouted very loudly!

g The mouse squeaked as it ran.

h The sun shone brightly.

i I ran down the street.

2 Complete each sentence with a verb that makes sense. Use the verbs in the box to help you.

a The giraffe _____ leaves from high branches.

b The dog _____ at the postman.

c My dad _____ very loudly!

d The teacher _____ her name on the board.

e The spider _____ in the corner.

f The horse _____ away.

g The cat _____ because it was happy.

h The waves _____ up the beach.

snores

purred

roared

ate

wrote

galloped

barked

lurked

Tenses

The words we write tell us whether things are happening now, in the past or in the future.

I am walking is the **present** – now.

I walked is in the **past**.

I shall walk is in the **future**.

1 Write whether these sentences are in the past, present or future tense.

a I sat on the chair. _____

b I went to the party. _____

c I'll see you in the morning. _____

d She saw a cat. _____

e I shall go to school tomorrow. _____

f I am laughing. _____

g I can see a rainbow! _____

h I ran all the way home. _____

i I am reading a great story. _____

j I am swimming. _____

2 Cross out the incorrect verb in each sentence.

a I **wented went** to school today.

b I **seen saw** a whale!

c Did you **see saw** that sunset?

d Who **ran runned** the fastest?

e I **won winned** the race!

f I **catched caught** the ball.

g He **seed saw** the film today.

h I **goed went** to my Granny's yesterday.

i I **caught catched** a cold.

Compound words

Compound words are made from smaller words **joined together**, without changing the spelling.

butter + fly = butterfly

1 Draw a line to match the parts of the compound words to make new words. The first one is done for you.

a news   lid

b sand   castle

c flower   bird

d lady   pot

e eye   paper

    f hand   case

    g bed   bag

    h stair   room

    i note   up

    j make   book

2 Use the words in the box to make 10 compound words.

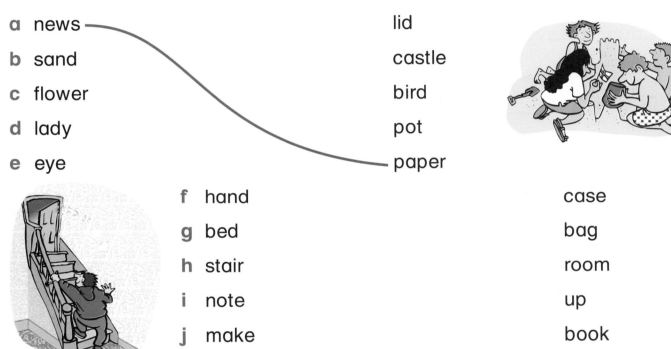

ball   crow   fish   board   stick   day   bull   skate   stack   week

a scare _____

b _____ board

c star _____

d cup _____

e hay _____

f birth _____

g _____ dog

h lip _____

i _____ end

j foot _____

Syllables

Syllables are the **chunks of sound** that make up words. If you say words out loud, you can hear the syllables.

bathroom has two syllables:

bath + room

crocodile has three syllables:

croc + o + dile

1 Count the syllables in each word. Then write the answer in the box.

a caterpillar ☐

b leaf ☐

c garden ☐

d rainbow ☐

e spider ☐

f butterfly ☐

g ladybird ☐

h bird ☐

i hedgehog ☐

j greenhouse ☐

2 Rewrite the words in order, with the word with the lowest number of syllables first.

a daisy rose buttercup _____ _____ _____

b chinchilla cat rabbit _____ _____ _____

c planet sun universe _____ _____ _____

d sausages eggs bacon _____ _____ _____

e orange banana lime _____ _____ _____

f pen pencil computer _____ _____ _____

g telephone mobile talk _____ _____ _____

h tea chocolate coffee _____ _____ _____

i sandwiches cake trifle _____ _____ _____

j scorpion ant beetle _____ _____ _____

Suffix *ful*

The letters *ful* can be added to the end of words as a suffix. When you add the suffix *ful* to a word, you are saying that it is **full of** something.

A spoon**ful** of sugar is a spoon **full of** sugar.

1 Write new words using the suffix *ful*.

a Full of hope [hope + ful] = _____

b Full of joy [joy + ful] = _____

c Full of peace [peace + ful] = _____

d Full of sorrow [sorrow + ful] = _____

e Full of colour [colour + ful] = _____

f Full of doubt [doubt + ful] = _____

g Full of cheer [cheer + ful] = _____

h Full of power [power + ful] = _____

i Full of thought [thought + ful] = _____

2 Write the meaning of each word. If you don't know, use a dictionary.

a wonderful _____

b playful _____

c useful _____

d helpful _____

e hopeful _____

f joyful _____

g truthful _____

h beautiful _____

i hateful _____

Suffix *ly*

In this sentence, the word *carefully* is an adverb. It tells **how** the girl made the model. The *ly* at the end is a suffix, added to the word *careful*. By adding *ly* we make an adverb that tells us how something happens or is done.

The girl made the model plane **carefully**.

1 Complete each sentence with the correct adverb from the box.

| happily   kindly   lazily   delicately   roughly   selfishly   sadly |

a The boy _____ shared his sweets.

b The cat stretched out _____ on the chair.

c My grandma smiled _____ when she saw me coming.

d The man frowned _____.

e The butterfly fluttered _____ from flower to flower.

f The boy _____ said he would not share his toys.

g The swimmer rubbed herself _____ with the towel.

2 Draw a line to match each adverb to the correct description.

a carefully   shining

b bravely   fast

c brightly   done with care

d beautifully   not afraid

e perfectly   not done well

f quickly   moving in a delicate way

g badly   done in a lovely way

h gracefully   absolutely correct

Suffixes *ment*, *ness*, *less*

Suffixes can be added to words to make new words.

The suffix *ment* can be added to pave to make pavement.

The suffix *ness* can be added to full to make fullness.

The suffix *less* can be added to time to make timeless.

1 Add the suffix to each word.

a base + ment = _____

b weight + less = _____

c bad + ness = _____

d end + less = _____

e cheerful + ness = _____

2 Draw a line to match each word to the correct suffix.

a move   ment

b bashful   ness

c enjoy   ment

d agree   less

e age   ment

Tricky spellings

Some words do not seem to follow spelling rules or are difficult to work out by saying them out loud. You just have to learn them by heart.

every　　*gnat*　　*neither*

1 **Learn these tricky words using the LOOK, COVER, WRITE, CHECK method.**

a only _____

b little _____

c down _____

d their _____

e because _____

f could _____

g would _____

h should _____

i does _____

j goes _____

2 **Spend a few minutes looking at each word. Cover it up. Then try to write it from memory. Check your spelling against the original.**

a mother _____

b father _____

c always _____

d once _____

e upon _____

f after _____

g every _____

h eight _____

i brother _____

j before _____

Writing stories (1) – plotting

Plotting a story is fun! You get to think about all of the exciting things that will happen in your story.

1 Think about your story by answering these questions.

a Who are your main characters?

_____

b Who are your supporting characters?

_____

c Where is your story set?

_____

d Will you use the weather to help to build the atmosphere?

_____

2 Now think about the action of your story.

a How will your story start? A good beginning will make your reader want to read the whole story, so make it exciting!

_____

b Is there a 'main event' in the story?

_____

c What is the main problem to be solved?

_____

d Think of a good, strong ending.

_____

Writing stories (2) – characters

Once you have a plot line, you need to start thinking about your characters. They are what bring your story to life!

1 Answer these questions about your main character to help you.

a What is your character's name?

_____

b What does your character look like?

_____

c What sort of clothes does your character wear? Does that give the reader hints about the sort of person they are?

_____

d What is your character's voice like?

_____

e What is your character's hair like?

_____

2 Now answer these questions to develop your character further.

a Where does your character live?

_____

b Does your character have any habits?

_____

c Does your character have a job?

_____

Writing shape poems

Shape poems are written in the shape of the subject of the poem. The subject is the main thing that the poem is about.

Like a blanket of silver floating silently upon high. glitter, decorating the dark night sky, a twinkling ocean of diamonds

1 Write a cloud poem. You can use some of the words in the box. Write your poem around the cloud outline.

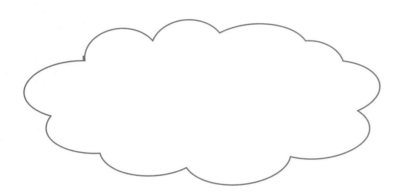

drip	mist
drift	drizzle
damp	float
dark	grey
deluge	pouring

2 Now write a flower poem. Make a list of words to use. Then write your poem around the flower outline.

_____

_____

_____

_____

_____

_____

Test 1 Adverbs

Adverbs tell you **how**, **when** or **where** action takes place.

Millie eats her dinner **greedily**.

Mum is **always** busy.

We like to play **outdoors**.

1 Circle the adverb in each pair of words.

1. quickly   quick

2. slowly   slow

3. noisy   noisily

4. often   cats

5. cake   never

6. nearby   jumped

7. ran   later

8. happily   can

9. nice   cheerfully

10. completely   sad

10
9
8
7
6
5
4
3
2
1

Colour in your score.

Test 2 Adjectives

Adjectives **describe** nouns.

The **shiny red** ladybird crawled along the leaf.

Underline the adjective in each sentence.

1. The big dog ran away.

2. The little mouse squeaked.

3. The tall man laughed loudly.

4. The tiny baby giggled quietly.

5. The long snake slithered across the ground.

6. The golden sun shone brightly.

7. The hairy spider scuttled up the wall.

8. The old woman wrote a letter.

9. The furry rabbit jumped high.

10. The brown worm wriggled under the leaves.

Colour in your score.

Test 3 Word order

We have to write words in the **correct order** so they make **sense**.

eat Monkeys bananas. ☒

Monkeys eat bananas. ☑

Write these sentences correctly.

1. milk. Cats drink _____

2. lay eggs. Birds _____

3. asleep. is dog The _____

4. balloon A pop. can _____

5. is The green. grass _____

6. A hop. frog can _____

7. red. My is coat best _____

8. swim pool. You a in _____

9. wash a You sink. in _____

10. tree tall. very The is _____

Colour in your score.

34

Test 4 Adding *ing* and *ed*

We can add *ing* and *ed* to the end of some words.

Yesterday I walk**ed** to school.

Today I am walk**ing** to the shops.

**Write these words so they end in *ing*.
Spell them correctly.**

1. miss   _____

2. shop   _____

3. write   _____

4. carry   _____

5. crash   _____

**Write these words so they end in *ed*.
Spell them correctly.**

6. beg   _____

7. blame   _____

8. copy   _____

9. splash   _____

10. rub   _____

School   Shop

10
9
8
7
6
5
4
3
2
1

Colour in your score.

Test 5 Making sense of sentences

Sentences must **make sense** when you read them.

The aeroplane *flied* in the sky. ☒
The aeroplane *flew* in the sky. ☑

Choose the correct word to finish each sentence.

1. The dog _____ the postman. (bit/bited)

2. The boy _____ the window. (breaked/broke)

3. I _____ the ball. (catched/caught)

4. I _____ the moon. (seed/saw)

5. The girl _____ reading. (is/are)

6. The children _____ running. (was/were)

7. My mum _____ home. (come/came)

8. I _____ in the shop. (went/goed)

9. I _____ got an apple. (has/have)

10. The boy _____ himself. (hurt/hurted)

Colour in your score.

Test 6 Conjunctions

A conjunction is a **joining** word. It may be used to join **two sentences** together.

EEK

A mouse is small. An elephant is big.

A mouse is small **but** an elephant is big.

Choose the conjunction *and* or *but* to fill each gap.

1. I picked up the apple _____ ate it.

2. The girl found her bag _____ went to school.

3. I got the sum right _____ Ben didn't.

4. The lion stopped _____ roared.

5. I like swimming _____ reading.

6. I sat down _____ watched TV.

7. This door is open _____ that door is shut.

8. Metal is hard _____ wool is soft.

9. I got undressed _____ went to bed.

10. I opened my bag _____ took out a book.

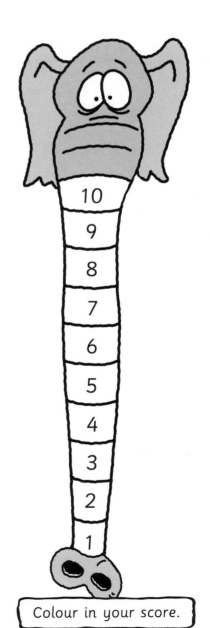

10
9
8
7
6
5
4
3
2
1

Colour in your score.

Test 7 Word building

In spelling we have to learn to **build** up words.

h + ow + l = howl

Do these sums. Write the words you make.

1. l + ou + d = _____

2. d + ow + n = _____

3. m + ou + th = _____

4. f + ou + nd = _____

5. cr + ow + d = _____

6. cl + ow + n = _____

7. sh + ou + t = _____

8. sp + ou + t = _____

9. fl + ow + er = _____

10. cr + ou + ch = _____

Colour in your score.

38

Test 8 Full stops and question marks

I live in a house.

Where do you live?

A **sentence** often ends with a **full stop**.

A **question** always ends with a **question mark**.

Rewrite each sentence correctly. Add capital letters, full stops and question marks in the correct places.

1. a farmer lives on a farm _____

2. why are you late _____

3. bees live in a hive _____

4. what is the matter _____

5. where is my pen _____

6. the fox ran quickly _____

7. the clouds were black _____

8. who is your friend _____

9. the wind is blowing _____

10. how did you do it _____

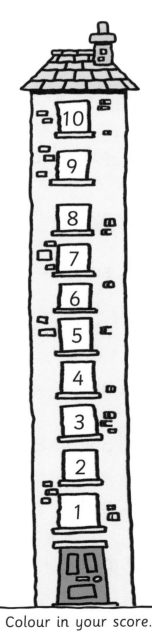

Colour in your score.

Test 9 Compound words

Compound words are made up of **two smaller words** joined together.

lady   +   bird   =   ladybird

Do the word sums and write the answers.

1. foot + ball = _____

2. rain + bow = _____

3. sun + shine = _____

4. snow + man = _____

5. play + time = _____

6. butter + fly = _____

7. bull + dog = _____

8. hedge + hog = _____

9. black + berry = _____

10. key + hole = _____

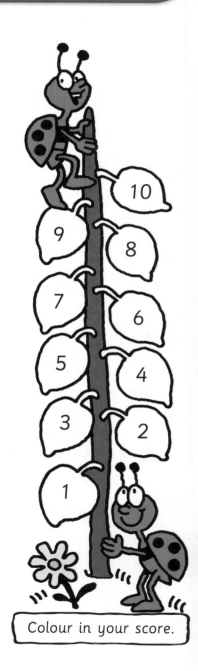

Colour in your score.

40

Test 10 Playing with words

You should always look for **patterns** and **similar spellings** in words – it helps you to learn to spell new words!

cake

rake   **sh**ake   lake

Write the new words you make.

1. Change the **f** in **f**air to **ch**.   _____

2. Change the **r** in **r**are to **fl**.   _____

3. Change the **t** in **t**ear to **b**.   _____

4. Change the **l** in **l**ord to **c**.   _____

5. Change the **j** in **j**aw to **cl**.   _____

6. Change the **c** in **c**ore to **sh**.   _____

7. Change the **w** in **w**ire to **f**.   _____

8. Change the **p** in **p**ure to **c**.   _____

9. Change the **f** in **f**ind to **w**.   _____

10. Change the **r** in **r**oar to **s**.   _____

10
9
8
7
6
5
4
3
2
1

Colour in your score.

Test 11 **Speech marks**

Speech marks, or inverted commas, show someone is **speaking**.
We write everything the person says **inside** the speech marks.

The postman said,
"I deliver letters."

Put in the missing speech marks.

1. The builder said, I use a hammer.

2. The driver said, I drive a big lorry.

3. I am feeling tired, said Mrs Smith.

4. The librarian said, I work in a library.

5. The farmer said, I keep cows on my farm.

6. The queen said, I wear a crown.

7. The nurse said, I work in a hospital.

8. My job is dangerous, said the firefighter.

9. The caretaker said, I keep the school clean.

10. I make bread, said the baker.

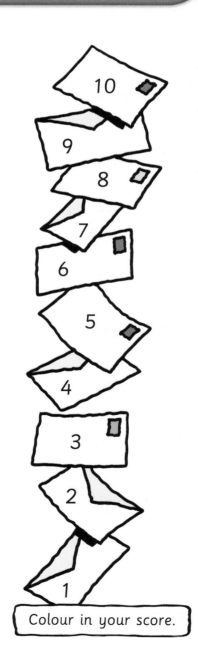

Colour in your score.

Test 12 What's going on?

All of these verbs (action words) describe **actions** that are going on in the past or present tense. Notice that they all end in *ing*.

Choose a verb from the box to complete each sentence. Think carefully about your answers to make sure every sentence makes sense.

crying	swimming	sitting	flying	sleeping
laughing	running	barking	baking	walking

1. I was _____ fast.

2. She is _____ slowly.

3. Mum was _____ down.

4. The dog was _____ fiercely.

5. The fish is _____ through the weeds.

6. A butterfly was _____ from flower to flower.

7. Nana was _____ my favourite cake.

8. My cat Layla was _____ in the sunshine.

9. Dad is _____ at a funny programme.

10. The baby was _____ so I picked her up.

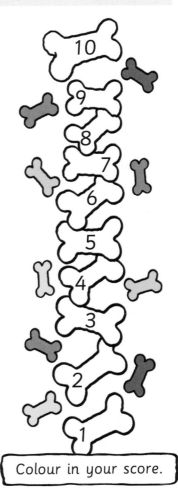

Colour in your score.

43

Test 13 Verbs

Verbs tell us what someone is **doing**.

A cow **moos**.

Choose the best verb to complete each sentence.

moos   clucks   purrs   neighs   hoots
squeaks   gobbles   bleats   quacks   barks

1. A cow _____.

2. An owl _____.

3. A hen _____.

4. A duck _____.

5. A turkey _____.

6. A horse _____.

7. A dog _____.

8. A sheep _____.

9. A mouse _____.

10. A cat _____.

Colour in your score.

44

Test 14 Checking your work

Always check your writing to see if you have made any silly mistakes.

goes
The rocket ~~go~~ fast.

Write the correct word to complete each sentence.

1. My uncle _____ very nice. (is/are)

2. The birds _____ very noisy. (was/were)

3. The children _____ reading. (is/are)

4. The girl _____ asleep. (was/were)

5. The cat _____ milk. (like/likes)

6. I _____ it well. (did/does)

7. My cousin _____ to visit. (comed/came)

8. I _____ my shirt. (teared/tore)

9. Tom always _____ hard at maths. (try/tries)

10. Lions _____. (roar/roars)

Colour in your score.

45

Test 15 Expanded noun phrases

You can make your writing more interesting by expanding noun phrases. A phrase is a **collection of words.**

The cat meowed. ➝ The **velvety black** cat meowed.

Make these sentences more exciting by expanding the noun phrases with descriptions.

1. The _____ frog croaked.

2. A _____ dog barked.

3. The _____ sun shone.

4. The _____ spider scuttled away.

5. A _____ dolphin swam past.

6. The _____ stars twinkled.

7. The _____ monster sang.

8. Some _____ hopped away.

9. A _____ lion roared.

10. The _____ teacher was cross.

10

9

8

7

6

5

4

3

2

1

Colour in your score.

46

Test 16 **Commas**

Commas are used to **separate** things in a **list**.
We **don't** use a comma before the word *and*.

sheep, duck, donkey and hen

Fill in the missing commas.

1. red yellow blue and green

2. lion tiger cheetah and leopard

3. apples pears bananas and grapes

4. pen pencil crayon and felt-tip

5. rain sun snow and fog

6. I saw a car a bus a lorry and a bike.

7. In my bag I took a mirror a ruler and a pencil.

8. I like oranges peaches cherries and melons.

9. I can play football cricket rugby and snooker.

10. A gardener needs a spade a fork a trowel and a hoe.

10
9
8
7
6
5
4
3
2
1

Colour in your score.

Test 17 Adding to the end of words

Sometimes we can change words by **adding letters** to the **end** of them.

The kitten likes to **play**. It is very play**ful**.

When *full* comes at the end of a word we spell it *ful*.

Do these word sums. Write the answers.

1. use + ful = _____

2. hope + ful = _____

3. help + ful = _____

4. pain + ful = _____

5. beauty + ful = _____

Take off *ful*. Write the word you are left with.

6. colourful _____

7. faithful _____

8. truthful _____

9. cheerful _____

10. plentiful _____

Colour in your score.

48

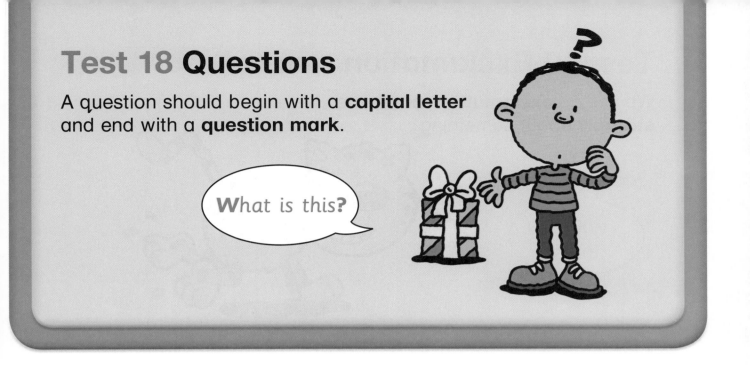

Test 18 Questions

A question should begin with a **capital letter** and end with a **question mark**.

What is this?

Rewrite each question correctly.

1. who looks after our teeth

   _____

2. what flies in the sky

   _____

3. where is your shirt

   _____

4. what do we use to dig with

   _____

5. who lives next door to you

   _____

6. where do we get milk from

   _____

7. why are you crying

   _____

8. how did you do that

   _____

9. who is your best friend

   _____

10. what makes a seed grow

    _____

Colour in your score.

Test 19 Exclamation marks

We use an **exclamation mark** when we feel **strongly** about something.

What a mess!

Rewrite each sentence. End each sentence with either a question mark or an exclamation mark.

1. come quickly   _____

2. who are you   _____

3. when did you arrive   _____

4. stop messing about   _____

5. what a nice surprise   _____

6. what are you doing   _____

7. you are horrible   _____

8. this cake tastes good   _____

9. why are you so upset   _____

10. shut that door   _____

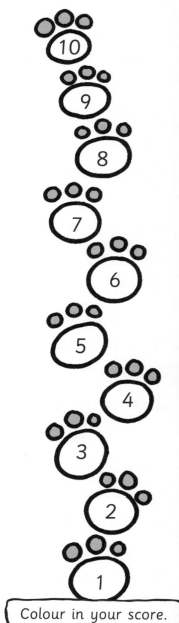

Colour in your score.

50

Test 20 Singular and plural

Singular means **one** thing. Plural means **more than one** thing.

one sweet   lots of sweets

Complete the phrases.

1. one rabbit, lots of _____

2. one chocolate, lots of _____

3. one wish, lots of _____

4. one cap, lots of _____

5. one pony, lots of _____

6. one _____ , lots of plates

7. one _____ , lots of horses

8. one _____ , lots of boxes

9. one _____ , lots of rockets

10. one _____ , lots of fairies

Colour in your score.

Test 21 Capital letters

We use a capital letter to **begin** the names of **people**,
the names of **days of the week** and **months of the year**.

My name is **S**hanaz.

My birthday is in **M**arch.

Write and spell correctly the name of some months.

The name of the months begining with *J*.

1. _____   2. _____

3. _____

The name of the months ending with *ber*.

4. _____   5. _____

6. _____   7. _____

The name of the months begining with *A*.

8. _____   9. _____

The name of the month begining with *F*.

10. _____

Colour in your score.

Test 22 Writing about real events

Writing about real life events is like being a newspaper reporter!

Write about an exciting day out. Answer the questions in full sentences.

1. Where did you go?

   _____

2. What time of year was it?

   _____

3. What was the weather like?

   _____

4. How did you travel?

   _____

5. What activities did you do?

   _____

6. What did you have for lunch?

   _____

7. Were there any special treats or snacks?

   _____

8. Did you see anything unusual?

   _____

9. Did you learn anything new?

   _____

10. Did you buy anything, such as a souvenir?

    _____

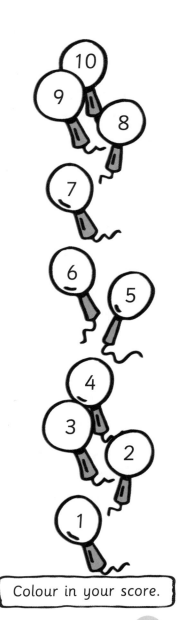

Colour in your score.

Test 23 Open ended questions

Open ended questions do not have one 'correct' answer – they want your views.

Read this story and answer the questions.

The door of the hutch swung open. The fox was waiting, and it chased the rabbit through the fence, out of the garden and into the open field. Jenny saw from her bedroom window, and she ran down the stairs. She shouted at the fox and leapt over the gate, chasing it. The rabbit hid in the bushes, and the fox tried to force its way in through the brambles.

"I'm coming, Flopsy!" Jenny called. "You go away, horrible fox!" As she got closer, the fox looked at her and ran a few steps backwards, and then it crept back towards the bushes, looking for the rabbit. Jenny waved her arms, and with a last look the fox ran away. Jenny crawled into the bushes and caught Flopsy, stroking her as she walked back to the house. "You are safe now," she said.

1. How do you think Jenny felt when she first saw the fox chasing the rabbit?

   _____

2. Why do you think the fox took a few steps backwards when it was shouted at?

   _____

3. Why do you think Jenny waved her arms?

   _____

4. How do you think Flopsy felt when she was hiding in the bushes?

   _____

5. How do you think Flopsy felt when Jenny picked her up and stroked her?

   _____

Colour in your score.

54

Test 24 Comprehension (1) – instructions

Instructions tell you what to do, so it is important that you can understand them.

Read these instructions for making pizza and answer the questions.

What to do:

1. Slice the mushrooms.
2. Spread the puree on the pizza base.
3. Add the mushrooms.
4. Grate the cheese and sprinkle on the top.
5. Sprinkle herbs over everything.
6. Bake the pizza in the oven until the cheese is slightly browned.

You need:

pizza base

tomato puree

cheddar cheese

mushrooms

herbs

1. Name three of the pizza ingredients.

   _____

2. What do you do with the mushrooms first?

   _____

3. How do you prepare the cheddar cheese?

   _____

4. What do you sprinkle on the pizza after the cheese, before baking?

   _____

5. How do you know when the pizza is ready?

   _____

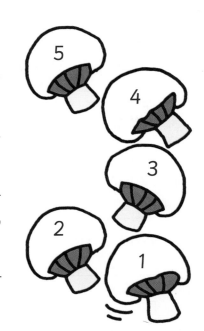

Colour in your score.

Test 25 Comprehension (2) – dialogue

Dialogue gives a reader lots of information, so it is important that you can understand what is being said.

Read the dialogue and answer the questions.

whooohhaaaa!!!!

"I loved that film! The scary queen was brilliant!"

"She was great. I really liked her spiky crown. I liked the purple dragon best though."

"The castle looked brilliant – especially the giant spiders in the dungeon."

"I thought the spiders were terrifying!"

"Oh yes – and that ghost hiding in the woods – very scary!"

"I really jumped when it popped out of the tree stump!"

"I nearly fell off my chair! I dropped some popcorn."

1. Where were the spiders?

   _____

2. What was hiding in the woods?

   _____

3. What colour was the dragon?

   _____

4. Where did the ghost pop out of?

   _____

5. What was the queen's crown like?

   _____

Colour in your score.

56

Comprehension exercises help you to see if you understand what you have read.

Read this passage and answer the questions.

Ladybirds are marvellous beetles. There are over 5000 species in the world and 46 species in Britain. They smell with their feet and produce smelly liquid from their knees to warn off predators. They can fly at speeds up to 15 miles per hour and flap their wings an amazing 85 times each second!

1. How many species of ladybirds are there in Britain?

   _____

2. What part of their bodies do ladybirds use to smell things?

   _____

3. Where does the liquid come from that ladybirds use to warn off predators?

   _____

4. What speed can ladybirds fly at?

   _____

5. How many times a second can ladybirds flap their wings?

   _____

Colour in your score.

Test 27 Comprehension (4) – traditional tales

Comprehension questions about a traditional tale can help you to see if you have really understood what you have read.

Read this part of a story and answer the questions.

Goldilocks was walking in the forest when she saw a cosy cottage in a clearing. As she knocked on the door, it creaked open, so she went inside.
In the kitchen, she could smell a delicious, creamy smell. Her tummy rumbled. Three bowls were sitting on the table. Goldilocks rushed across the room, and popped a spoon into the first bowl of porridge. She scooped up a blob of porridge and stuffed it in her mouth.
"Ew! Too cold!" she cried. She saw a second bowl of porridge and tried again.
"Ow! Too hot!" she yelped. She saw a third bowl of porridge and tried again.
"Oh yum!" she smiled. "Delicious – it's just right!"

1. Where was Goldilocks walking?

   _____

2. What did she see in a clearing?

   _____

3. What could she smell in the kitchen?

   _____

4. What was wrong with the first bowl of porridge?

   _____

5. What did she think of the last bowl of porridge?

   _____

5
4
3
2
1

Colour in your score.

Test 28 Comprehension (5) – fictional narrative

Comprehension questions about a story help you to see if you have understood what you have read.

Read this story and answer the questions.

The mermaid hid in the kelp forest. She felt the tiny fish tickling her as they slipped backwards and forwards round her tail. She could see the dolphin searching for her under rocks and in piles of shells, and she giggled to herself. A passing seal winked at her as he rushed towards the surface.

1. Who was hiding in the kelp?

   _____

2. What tickled her tail?

   _____

3. Who was looking for her?

   _____

4. What creature winked at the mermaid?

   _____

5. Where was the seal going?

   _____

5

4

3

2

1

Colour in your score.

Test 29 **Writing *ai, ar, un***

It is important to practise your handwriting so that people can read all the good things you write about!

ai ar un

Write these *ai*, *ar* and *un* words. Use your best joined-up handwriting.

1. chair _____

2. train _____

3. drain _____

4. fairy _____

5. bark _____

6. shark _____

7. start _____

8. bun _____

9. fun _____

10. under _____

Colour in your score.

60

Test 30 Writing *ab*, *ul*, *it*

Some handwriting patterns are difficult, because they join a small letter to a tall letter.

ab ul it

Write these *ab*, *ul* and *it* words. Use your best joined-up handwriting.

1. about _____

2. baby _____

3. table _____

4. rabbit _____

5. pull _____

6. bull _____

7. full _____

8. bit _____

9. bite _____

10. hit _____

Colour in your score.

61

ANSWERS

Page 2

1. **a** A description of the size of your child's family (sisters, brothers, cousins, etc.)
   b A description of where family members live (adult siblings, grandparents, parents, etc.)
   c A discussion of jobs that adults in the family do, if any
   d A discussion of things the family enjoys doing
   e A picture of the family

2. Your child should describe their favourite toy – what it is like, why it is the favourite, how it is played with, etc.

Page 3

1. Your child should answer the questions about their pet – or the pet they would like to have.

2. Your child should explain how to draw a house.

Page 4

1. **a** bridge   **e** stage
   b image   **f** judge
   c village   **g** rage
   d nudge

2. **a** fudge   **e** edge
   b lodge   **f** fridge
   c page   **g** dodge
   d package

Page 5

1. Make sure your child has drawn a line to match each word to its picture.
   a knot   **e** gnat
   b knitting   **f** knight
   c gnome   **g** knuckle
   d knife

2. Any sentences which make sense.
   a knock   **d** gnash
   b gnaw   **e** gnu
   c know

Page 6

1. Make sure your child has drawn a line to match each word to its picture.
   a wreck
   b write
   c wrist
   d wrinkle
   e wrap
   f wreath

2. wren, writer, wrestler, wriggle, wrong, wrench

Page 7

1. Make sure your child has learnt the correct spellings.

2. **a** pupil   **e** metal
   b total   **f** signal
   c civil   **g** evil
   d pencil   **h** fossil

Page 8

1. **a** eagle   **f** hotel
   b tunnel   **g** little
   c maple   **h** giggle
   d angel/angle **i** chapel
   e simple

2. **a** double   **e** castle
   b handle   **f** flannel
   c squirrel   **g** channel
   d beetle

Page 9

1. **a** skies   **e** spies
   b countries **f** jellies
   c berries   **g** ladies
   d bodies   **h** studies

2. **a** party   **e** enemy
   b pony   **f** city
   c puppy   **g** cherry
   d story   **h** fly

3. puppies, jelly, cherries

Page 10

1. **a** whale   **f** chips
   b chimp   **g** chilly
   c whisk   **h** wheat
   d chair   **i** whistle
   e whiteboard

2. **a** What   **c** Which
   b Who   **d** Why

Page 11

1. **a** beautiful
   b loneliness
   c happily

2. **a** hiking
   b shiny
   c nicest

3. **a** humming   **d** fatter
   b dropped   **e** runny
   c saddest

Page 12

1. **a** I'll   **f** beach
   b aloud   **g** pear
   c eight   **h** creak
   d eye   **i** deer
   e bare

2. Cross out:
   a groan   **e** hole
   b hare   **f** Hour
   c two   **g** no
   d heard   **h** mown

Page 13

1. **a** can't   **e** I'm
   b won't   **f** I'd
   c isn't   **g** I'll
   d don't   **h** couldn't

2. **a** I'd   **e** It's
   b can't   **f** didn't
   c I'll   **g** don't

Page 14

1. **a** audition   **f** infection
   b celebration **g** rotation
   c caution   **h** suction
   d collection   **i** hibernation
   e reflection   **j** tradition

2. **a** auction   **e** action
   b tuition   **f** fiction
   c operation   **g** exhibition
   d station

Page 15

1. **a** dog's   **e** boy's
   b girl's   **f** woman's
   c man's   **g** baby's
   d horse's

2. **a** dogs'   **e** cats'
   b girls'   **f** bats'
   c birds'   **g** boys'
   d puppies'

Page 16

1. **a** E   **d** E
   b Q   **e** E
   c Q   **f** Q

2. **a** S   **d** Q
   b E   **e** S
   c Q   **f** Q

Page 17

1. **a** I like cats, dogs and rabbits.
   b I read books, comics and newspapers.
   c My favourite foods are cake, toast and oranges.
   d I collected shells, stones and seaweed to decorate my sandcastle.
   e Rainbows are red, orange, yellow, green, blue, indigo and violet.
   f It is cold so put on a hat, scarf and gloves.
   g I drink orange juice, cola and milk.
   h I saw tigers, lions and hippos at the zoo.

2. Any sensible sentences including lists (with commas) about the subjects given.

Page 18

1.
a What is your name?
b "Can I come too?" asked Mary.
c Why can't I? That's not fair!
d Would you like a sweet?
e Why not? I want to!
f Do you like snakes?
g Do you want to come with me? I don't mind.
h Can we go today?
i Who was that?
j Would anyone like some supper?

2.
a Who
b Where
c What
d Why, Where or When
e What
f Where
g When
h Who
i When or Where
j What

Page 19

1.
a cat, dog, elephant
b cake, pie, sandwich
c apple, orange, pear
d baby, child, toddler
e cup, plate, spoon

2.
a Ben, Lucy, Peter
b Jake, Nora, Selma
c Alex, Rajan, Tom
d Charlie, Marissa, Pat
e Lena, Nicholas, Sophia

Page 20

1. There is no right way to segment these words; your child should break them down in any way that makes them easy to remember. Here are some suggestions:
a sn - ail
b writ - ing
c ho - tel
d may - be
e don - key
f flow - ers
g car - rot
h imp - ort - ant
i com - put - er

2.
a ou
b oth
c se
d dow
e an
f j-ping
g ter
h oth - er

Page 21

1.
a flew
b laughed
c ate
d slid
e roared
f shouted
g squeaked
h shone
i ran

2.
a ate
b barked
c snores
d wrote
e lurked
f galloped
g purred
h roared

Page 22

1.
a past
b past
c future
d past
e future
f present
g present
h past
i present
j present

2. Cross out:
a wented
b seen
c saw
d runned
e winned
f catched
g seed
h goed
i catched

Page 23

1.
a paper
b castle
c pot
d bird
e lid
f bag
g room
h case
i book
j up

2.
a scarecrow
b skateboard
c starfish
d cupboard
e haystack
f birthday
g bulldog
h lipstick
i weekend
j football

Page 24

1.
a 4
b 1
c 2
d 2
e 2
f 3
g 3
h 1
i 2
j 2

2.
a rose daisy buttercup
b cat rabbit chinchilla
c sun planet universe
d eggs bacon sausages
e lime orange banana
f pen pencil computer
g talk mobile telephone
h tea coffee chocolate
i cake trifle sandwiches
j ant beetle scorpion

Page 25

1.
a hopeful
b joyful
c peaceful
d sorrowful
e colourful
f doubtful
g cheerful
h powerful
i thoughtful

2. Any correct answers. Some suggestions are given below:
a fabulous; a really good thing.
b messing about in a happy way; playing games.
c something that can be used to carry out jobs; just what is needed.
d someone who is willing to help and make themselves useful.
e full of hope (perhaps that something will or will not happen).
f very happy.
g does not lie; tells the truth.
h lovely; attractive.
i horrid; nasty.

Page 26

1.
a kindly
b lazily
c happily
d sadly
e delicately
f selfishly
g roughly

2.
a done with care
b not afraid
c shining
d done in a lovely way
e absolutely correct
f fast
g not done well
h moving in a delicate way

Page 27

1.
a basement
b weightless
c badness
d endless
e cheerfulness

2.
a movement
b bashfulness
c enjoyment
d agreement
e ageless

Page 28

1. Make sure your child has learnt and can spell the words correctly.

2. Make sure your child has learnt and can spell the words correctly.

Page 29

1.
a A description of main characters
b A description of supporting characters
c A description of where the story is set
d A description of the weather and how it will be used to build atmosphere

2.
a A good story starter
b A description of the main event of the story
c A description of the main problem
d A good strong ending

Page 30

1.
a Name of main character
b Description of character
c Description of clothes and how they might hint at the nature of the character
d Description of character's voice
e Description of hair/hairdo

2.
a Description of the character's home
b Description of any special habits
c Description of character's job

Page 31

1. A 'shape' poem about a cloud, using some or all of the words in the box.
2. A list of words to use in a poem about flowers. A 'shape' poem about a flower written on the shape provided.

Page 32

1. quickly
2. slowly
3. noisily
4. often
5. never
6. nearby
7. later
8. happily
9. cheerfully
10. completely

Page 33

1. big
2. little
3. tall
4. tiny
5. long
6. golden
7. hairy
8. old
9. furry
10. brown

ANSWERS

Page 34
1. Cats drink milk.
2. Birds lay eggs.
3. The dog is asleep.
4. A balloon can pop.
5. The grass is green.
6. A frog can hop.
7. My best coat is red.
8. You swim in a pool.
9. You wash in a sink.
10. The tree is very tall.

Page 35
1. missing
2. shopping
3. writing
4. carrying
5. crashing
6. begged
7. blamed
8. copied
9. splashed
10. rubbed

Page 36
1. bit
2. broke
3. caught
4. saw
5. is
6. were
7. came
8. went
9. have
10. hurt

Page 37
1. and
2. and
3. but
4. and
5. and
6. and
7. but/and
8. but/and
9. and
10. and

Page 38
1. loud
2. down
3. mouth
4. found
5. crowd
6. clown
7. shout
8. spout
9. flower
10. crouch

Page 39
1. A farmer lives on a farm.
2. Why are you late?
3. Bees live in a hive.

4. What is the matter?
5. Where is my pen?
6. The fox ran quickly.
7. The clouds were black.
8. Who is your friend?
9. The wind is blowing.
10. How did you do it?

Page 40
1. football
2. rainbow
3. sunshine
4. snowman
5. playtime
6. butterfly
7. bulldog
8. hedgehog
9. blackberry
10. keyhole

Page 41
1. chair
2. flare
3. bear
4. cord
5. claw
6. shore
7. fire
8. cure
9. wind
10. soar

Page 42
1. The builder said, "I use a hammer."
2. The driver said, "I drive a big lorry."
3. "I am feeling tired," said Mrs Smith.
4. The librarian said, "I work in a library."
5. The farmer said, "I keep cows on my farm."
6. The queen said, "I wear a crown."
7. The nurse said, "I work in a hospital."
8. "My job is dangerous," said the firefighter.
9. The caretaker said, "I keep the school clean."
10. "I make bread," said the baker.

Page 43
1. running
2. walking
3. sitting
4. barking
5. swimming
6. flying
7. baking
8. sleeping
9. laughing
10. crying

Page 44
1. moos
2. hoots
3. clucks
4. quacks
5. gobbles
6. neighs
7. barks
8. bleats
9. squeaks
10. purrs

Page 45
1. is
2. were
3. are
4. was
5. likes
6. did
7. came
8. tore
9. tries
10. roar

Page 46
Any sensible and interesting description for each noun mentioned, to make the sentence more exciting.
e.g. The slippery green frog croaked.

Page 47
1. red, yellow, blue and green
2. lion, tiger, cheetah and leopard
3. apples, pears, bananas and grapes
4. pen, pencil, crayon and felt-tip
5. rain, sun, snow and fog
6. I saw a car, a bus, a lorry and a bike.
7. In my bag I took a mirror, a ruler and a pencil.
8. I like oranges, peaches, cherries and melons.
9. I can play football, cricket, rugby and snooker.
10. A gardener needs a spade, a fork, a trowel and a hoe.

Page 48
1. useful
2. hopeful
3. helpful
4. painful
5. beautiful
6. colour
7. faith
8. truth
9. cheer
10. plenty

Page 49
1. Who looks after our teeth?
2. What flies in the sky?
3. Where is your shirt?
4. What do we use to dig with?
5. Who lives next door to you?
6. Where do we get milk from?
7. Why are you crying?
8. How did you do that?
9. Who is your best friend?
10. What makes a seed grow?

Page 50
1. Come quickly!
2. Who are you?
3. When did you arrive?
4. Stop messing about!
5. What a nice surprise!
6. What are you doing?
7. You are horrible!
8. This cake tastes good!
9. Why are you so upset?
10. Shut that door!

Page 51
1. rabbits
2. chocolates
3. wishes
4. caps
5. ponies
6. plate
7. horse
8. box
9. rocket
10. fairy

Page 52
Answers 1–3, 4–7 and 8–9 can be given in any order.
1. January
2. June
3. July
4. September
5. October
6. November
7. December
8. April
9. August
10. February